THE OLYMPIC DISCUS

THE
OLYMPIC DISCUS

A Story of Ancient Greece

JAN PARANDOWSKI

Introduction by George Harjan

FREDERICK UNGAR PUBLISHING CO.
NEW YORK

Translated from the Polish by
A. M. Malecka and S. A. Walewski

INTRODUCTION

Jan Parandowski, one of the greatest of contemporary Polish writers, was born on May 11, 1895 in Lvov, at that time part of the Austro-Hungarian Empire, to the family of an official of the provincial government. His literary debut dates from his last year in a *gymnasium,* a strict classical institution, in which the future writer received a solid foundation for his interest in Greek and Latin cultures. His first book, a study of Rousseau, appeared shortly before his matriculation in 1913; it gave early indications of Parandowski's liking for the genres of biography and short story.

The First World War cut short his studies at Lvov University; Russian troops entered the city, and since he was of draft age and an Austrian subject, he was forced to move to Central Russia, where he was a civilian internee. After the revolution in Russia, he returned to his native city and resumed his studies at the university, eventually graduating in classical literature, philosophy, and archeology. At the same time he contributed to the *Gazeta Lwowska* as a writer and theatre critic.

Parandowski's interest in antiquity led first to publication in 1923 of *Mitologia* [Mythology], a popularization of Greek myths for children which became a Polish classic, and later in the same year to its frivolous marginalia, *Eros na Olimpie* [Eros on Olympus], a ribald classic depicting various amorous adventures of the Greek gods. Travel in Greece in 1925 further enriched his knowledge of the ancient world.

In 1936 Parandowski broke new ground in *Niebo w plo-mieniach* [Heaven in Flames], his best and most widely known work, a psychological novel on a subject hitherto unknown in Polish literature: the religious crisis in the soul of a young boy. The novel provoked keen criticism and controversy among Catholics and writers of the right. Its main character reappeared as a grown man in *Powrot do Zycia* [Return to Life] (1961), but this novel dealt chiefly with wartime conditions, as did *Wrzesniowa Noc* [September Night] (1962); the latter depicted Parandowski's personal experiences during the nightmare of the German occupation of Poland, where he remained during the war, finally being forced into hiding. After liberation by Soviet troops he became a professor of comparative literature at Lublin Catholic University. During the postwar years and through the 1950's, Parandowski revealed his versatility and the wide range of his interests in a variety of short stories and essays.

The theme of antiquity and the traditional subjects of European culture predominate in Parandowski's writings. Despite the tremendous upheavals in the world in the last few decades, disasters and catastrophes seem to have affected him but little; he is optimistic in his writings and always seeks for harmony. This equanimity is also evident in Parandowski's style, which is noted for its fecundity and pithiness. His prose is at times rhythmic and is characterized by the plasticity of its images. Ideologically he occupies a detached, seemingly neutral position and considers himself a realist; he is often called a contemporary Polish humanist. His firm and intransigent independence has earned him considerable respect both at home and abroad. As president of the Polish PEN (since 1933) and vice-president of the International PEN (since 1962), Parandowski has travelled extensively in Europe and South America, often meeting the most prominent European and American writers. He now lives in Warsaw.

Dysk Olimpijski (The Olympic Discus), the only novel of Parandowski translated into English, is a brilliant example of his interest both in travel and in classical antiquity. Before writing *The Olympic Discus,* he went to Greece again in 1932, in order to collect his material. He had the idea of investigating a new subject, sport in Ancient Greece. From this specific situation Parandowski attempted a reconstruction of the total picture of life in Ancient Greece.

When asked by friends and critics why he wrote about sports, Parandowski pointed out that athletics played an extremely important role in the life of the ancient Greeks. Plato was an athlete, as were Euripides and many other poets, playwrights, and philosophers. To get the physical perception of the site, what Shakespeare calls "the very age and body of the time," Parandowski arrived in 1932 at Olympia, an insignificant spot on the tourists' itinerary; he spent several weeks there, scrupulously measuring everything and reviewing the physical details of the stadium. All of the ruins of the stadia in Olympia were, however, of a later date than those of the period which Parandowski set out to describe. No remnants of the original circumambience existed, and he did not want to discuss the "reconstructed" Olympia.

The most ancient accounts place the origin of the Olympic Games, the most important events in the calendars of the ancient Greeks, at the time of Kronos. The event was to take place every five years, changed later to four. It was so important an occurrence that the time interval of four years between the games was called the Olympiad. The oldest known historical record dates back to 776 B.C., when

Lykurgos and Iphitos reintroduced the Games. At first the program was limited to one day, and consisted of one entry, a race the length of the stadium; later wrestling, javelin and discus throwing, chariot races, both of horses and mules, and the pentathlon were added. Plutarch says in his *Lives,* ". . . some . . . say that he [Lykurgos] flourished in the time of Iphitus [sic] and that they two jointly contrived the ordinance for the cessation of arms during the solemnity of the Olympic Games. Of this opinion was Aristotle and for confirmation of it he alleges an inscription upon one of the copper quoits used in the sport, upon which the name of Lykurgus continued uneffaced to his time."*

A sacred truce was proclaimed by special heralds, *spondophoroi,* first in Elis and then in the rest of the country, with the competitors coming from all over Greece and its colonies. Barbarians were prohibited from participation, but any free Greek whose hands were unsoiled by any crime could take part in the Games. Women were excluded not only from the Games but from the stadium too, save the virgins and priestesses of the goddess Demeter.

There were many spectators as well as performers, and the Games were an occasion for the congregation for traders, poets, and artists. The solemnities and the competition, and the ensuing festivities with the performance of religious rites and sacrifices, continued for five days. The entire competition consisted of twenty-four events, eighteen for adults and six for young boys. As the number of entries grew, the period of the Games was extended to seven days. The judges or referees, whose number varied from century to century, were called *hellanodikai.* They directed all the Games with the help of a special police force. Before their public appearance each of the competitors had to take an oath in front of

*Plutarch, *Lives,* New York, Modern Library, 1932, page 49

the statue of Zeus, that they had trained for their sports for ten months prior to the Games and that they were not guilty of any crime. They also had to swear that they would not resort to any trick or ruse, would not accept a bribe, and would uphold the spirit of the Olympic Games. Thirty days before the competition, all of the participants had to show their skill in the gymnasium before the *hellanodikai*. As a reward the victor was given a wreath made from a branch of a wild olive tree, placed on a bronze tripod, and given palm leaves to hold in his hands; this was the greatest honour bestowed upon any mortal.

Kings competed alongside commoners. The honours went not only to an individual himself, but to the state or to the city whence he originated; the records show that besides praise as national heroes and glorification by the poets, many a winner was able to derive some financial gain from his victories. To a Spartan, victory had a special significance. Plutarch reports that efforts were made to bribe a certain Spartan so that he would abstain from the competition. Having rejected the proposal and having won the simple wreath, he was asked what he had gained from his victory. "To have the right to fight next to my king," was the proud reply. The skill, the gracefulness, the beauty of the performance were just as highly esteemed as the victory itself.

This brief description of the Olympic Games offers a framework for Parandowski's *Olympic Discus,* which is divided into two parts: "In a Gymnasium" and "Olympia." The first depicts the preparations for the Games with a meticulous presentation of historical background and of physical setting. The atmosphere is of paramount importance. The author gives an exact and highly detailed account of the stadium, the sports equipment, and the various sports events. Were it not for Parandowski's dexterity in handling the material and for his brilliance of style, the surfeit of physical details would make this part desultory and incondite, but the writer admirably controls his material; his narrative is taut, and with the greatest economy of means he creates a series of images reminiscent of pictures on ancient Grecian vases.

At the beginning of the book the truce is proclaimed and Parandowski introduces an Athens that reflects a version of its past; the narrative acquires a solemn and somewhat legendary character. Before the spectators (for this is what one is tempted to call the readers) unfold the past and the traditions of the Olympic Games: "The time-honoured words, rendered still more dignified by the flowing utterance of the Olympic priest, reiterated for the seventy-sixth time the sacred covenant which Iphitos of Elis, Kleisthenes of Pisa, and Lycurgos of Sparta, kings who ruled when the legends were born, had concluded and inscribed upon a bronze disc at the beginning of history. In the memory of the listeners writhed the sharp lettering of the inscription which, resembling a serpent, the divine symbol of eternity, followed a coiled course upon the surface of the circular bronze, from its rim to the centre. For three centuries Olympia had called with the same voice. Every fourth year it would intrude between Wrath and Altercation the stadium's gleaming torch."

It was the seventy-sixth Olympiad in the year 476 B.C. which Parandowski sets out to describe. Why 476? Because, the writer claimed, this classical period lacked the banality of the later periods depicted in numerous textbooks, histories, and poems. Furthermore, he wanted to show a happy time, Olympia at a time of triumph, joy, and enthusiasm. The roads were free and the countryside peaceful, yet the city of Athens was almost in ruins; it had just recently withstood the onslaught of the Persians. In the Agora the population still remembered it: "It had taken place at a time when Xerxes crossed the frontiers of Greece—480 B.C.— the time of the last Olympic Games." Despite the gloom of the last festival the forthcoming Games had all the promises of being exciting. The *spondophoroi* set out to visit distant lands and inform the populace of the forthcoming event. The following chapter, "The Country of the Eternal Alliance" deals with Olympia itself. It is a combination of physical details put into historical settings; here Parandowski the historian prevails. Suddenly he moves his readers from reminiscence into reality: young athletes arrive, the aspirants undergo all the rigors of preparation for the games— history acquires flesh and substance.

Many a critic has been at a loss to classify *The Olympic Discus* since its first publication. To what genre did it belong? It was hardly appropriate to call it a novel; some considered it a *nouvelle;* yet there is a unifying idea in the book, and its seeming "plotlessness" is perhaps its most charming attribute. There are several vital characters in the book, among them Sotion; he at once commands our sympathy and undivided attention. Because of his physical skill and strength he is chosen as one of the adult competitors. Together with his friend Sodamos, he trains vigorously for the Games. Here we encounter the central problem of the work. To Sotion Parandowski juxtaposes a new kind of hero, who represents a different philosophy, incomprehensible and alien. Ikkos, the new aspirant, strikes the rest of the participants as singularly queer in his behaviour. His eating and drinking habits are different from the rest of the boys; his actions betray individualism and nonconformity. The astonishment of the participants grows, for after ordinary irri-

tation caused by Ikkos' behaviour, they discern in him a
sly and methodical man. It is up to Sotion, who, like Ikkos,
comes from Tarent, to untangle the web of mystery and
riddle. Sotion, the ephebe, "vowed to no aim and singularly
unencumbered," who "shone like a strayed fragment of the
Golden Age, giving out the gleam of his happy and purposeless life," challenges Ikkos' ideas, and claims that the latter
is overstepping the limit of an athletic ideal. This conversation is perhaps the culminating point in this conflict, which
is to acquire "cosmic proportions."

Parandowski is very strict in the construction of his work.
He does not permit any discordant note; his book is sym-
metrical, with both parts evenly balanced against each other.
In the first it is the conflict and the showdown between the
unencumbered Sotion and the practical Ikkos; in the second
it is the discus-throwing itself. The second part begins with a
digression about the entire Greek world (a favourite device
of Parandowski to present a picture of catholicity only to
turn to the specific). Immediately after, the second day of
the Games at the Hippodrome begins with several horse
races, as beautiful and exciting as any modern race. The
pentathlon begins with a single race and Sotion is doing
well. His jump provokes more attention; his gracefulness
dazzles the spectators. Now comes the culminating point of
The Olympic Discus: three quoits are brought in and the
competitors take their turns with them. It is a solemn moment. The quoits are old, as old as the original discus with
inscriptions. The throw is depicted with an almost unbeliev-
able plasticity and motion; it is indeed Myron's sculpture
coming to life. The last event in the competition is wrestling,
and the sly, methodical Ikkos, for whom the Games are more
than a cult, in fact a profession, is pitted against the care-

free but weary Sotion, for whom perfection had always been a favour of the gods. Out of this final combat emerges the victor.

Parandowski's persistent preoccupation with antiquity is discernible in most of his works; there is constant projection from modern times to the past and back again. This is particularly true of *The Olympic Discus*. Its epilogue is a cursory description of the subsequent development of the Olympic Games, when sport acquired a new meaning, became spectators' athletics, and, losing its athletic ideals, succumbed to the triumph of Ikkos' ideas. This development and decadence of athletics had a striking similarity with modern custom; athletes were pampered and groomed with the greatest of care, their diets, weights and habits watched. No longer was it a requisite to be a Greek to participate in the events; the Olympic Games were, to use a modern term, "big business." The epilogue is reminiscent of the conclusion of Anatole France's *Penguin Island;* Parandowski is mildly sceptical of our civilization. The book ends with a nostalgic note; when the Olympic Games are re-established in the late nineteenth century "the spirit of Greek agonistics begins its second life to repeat once more all former virtues and errors."

Parandowski took one single instance in Greek history, but by giving it a historical background, he placed it against a wider canvas of Greek life. He states that he took the names of his heroes from Pindar and from various writers of Byzantium. Homer's verses are quoted frequently by the characters in the story; Pindar is mentioned, and Themistocles arrives at the Games. The writer displays an amazing ability in depicting physical details, but his most important achievement is his plasticity in physical portraits and in describing the human body in motion.

At the Olympic Games in Berlin in 1936, over the protests of the Germans, Parandowski was awarded a bronze medal for his *Olympic Discus*, which achieved great popularity in Poland. This also introduced Parandowski to the Western European reader; it was his first major work to be translated into several languages. Preparations were made then to have it translated into German. The translation was duly executed and the German firm, Gurlitt Verlag, was to have published it. In 1939 the entire edition was ordered destroyed. The translator died during the German occupation of Poland, and the publishing house was bombed out during the war.

It was only after the war that the German translation of *The Olympic Discus* was published, first in Switzerland, then in the German Democratic Republic, and finally in the Federal Republic of Germany. By a remarkable coincidence, an English translation of the book appeared in London in September, 1939, a month memorable for all Poles. Parandowski knew nothing of it until 1943; word was sent to him through a friend who met a Polish patriot dropped by parachute into Poland, and who, among other things, passed the news of the English translation. The writer hardly had a chance to give this translation a second thought. However, in 1946, at the first postwar PEN Congress, he narrated this adventure to the British writer Storm Jameson, who was greatly surprised that the author had had no chance to see his work in translation and promised her good offices to obtain a copy for him. Shortly afterward, Parandowski, who was lingering in Sweden, received a note from Miss Jameson that no copies of *The Olympic Discus* were available and that the publishing house through which it had appeared no longer existed. There remained only one way to obtain a copy: to write to *The Times* and appeal to

Parandowski's readers. To his great delight readers began to respond, and several copies were sent to him. Letters came to him not only from Britain but from other countries of the British Commonwealth as well. "It was pleasant indeed," wrote Parandowski later, "to realize that in those trying days, under the German occupation, my book had access to distant homes of strangers and possessed a freedom of which I could not then even dare to dream."

George Harjan

York University and
University of Toronto
April, 1964

CONTENTS

Part One: IN THE GYMNASIUM

Part Two: OLYMPIA

PART ONE

IN THE GYMNASIUM

CHAPTER I

O N an Athenian morning of surpassing freshness the deep tones of the spondophoros's voice echoed with an imposing resonance, breaking the silence that had been spread by the city's trumpeter among the crowds which he had summoned at the first peep of dawn. In the statue-like stillness that supervened, the Agora quadrangle, brightening with the light of day, received the proclamation of a great forthcoming festival.

Olympia was to receive competitors and spectators in the Elean month of Parthenios, at the full of the third moon after the summer solstice. Every free-born Greek undefiled by the taint of homicidal guilt and with no curse of the gods upon his head was eligible by virtue of his civic rights to compete in the Games. And throughout the world the Truce of the Gods would prevail: nowhere would there be any crime, no stain from the shedding of blood, nor any disturbance from the noise of arms. This would apply, above all, to the Elean soil, to the sacred grove of Zeus, and to the time and place at which the Games would be held.

The time-honoured words, rendered still more dignified by the flowing utterance of the Olympic priest, reiterated for the seventy-sixth time the sacred covenant which Iphitos of Elis, Kleisthenes of Pisa, and Lycurgos of

Sparta, kings who ruled when the legends were born, had concluded and inscribed upon a bronze disc at the beginning of history. In the memory of the listeners writhed the sharp lettering of the inscription which, resembling a serpent, the divine symbol of eternity, followed a coiled course upon the surface of the circular bronze, from its rim to the centre. For three centuries Olympia had called with the same voice. Every fourth year it would intrude between Wrath and Altercation the stadium's gleaming torch. It would cause swords to be discarded and compel foemen to pay homage, unarmed, at the same altar. Through twelve generations the celestial signs had guided its reckoning of time; it had counted the moons and, at this one particular phase, from the mystic lunar chalice it had always dispensed peace.

The oration of the spondophoros, sentence by sentence, disarmed countries, cities, mountains and shores. Hellas, divided into so many small communities, each enclosed by frontiers, walls and ramparts, each living in the isolation of its own laws and customs, with hereditary feuds rankling within, opened out and became a free space traversed by the highways and paths which the divine command had endowed with safety. It paralysed even the brigands in the mountain passes, even the barbarians who bowed not to the worship of Zeus, for every Greek took upon himself the duty of proceeding against those who by any violence whatsoever would bar the road to Olympia. A period of universal armistice supervened. Proclaimed in the spring, it was to last until the autumn, thus binding together the two most sacred seasons of the year: the first when the heavens give their promise and the second when that promise is fulfilled.

The spondophoros stood on a pile of ruins which was transformed, as it were, into a pedestal of marble by his noble figure and the dignity of his office. The Agora in itself was virtually nothing but a geometrical illusion of four intersected angles, while the avenue of plane-trees with their charred trunks scarcely gave any inkling of spring. Among the neglected remnants of the Acropolis the dark pile of the temples stood out prominently against the pellucid skies. The scar caused by the conflagration of the Persian war was healing slowly amidst the lime and new bricks, the smell of which hovered over the town that had been hurriedly raised, its buildings ranging from insignificant hovels to walls freshly erected with prodigious toil.

These were to be seen here and there in the emptiness of the disorganised streets, surmounting rough foundations of huddled stones, broken columns and shattered statues. In them was thrust all that had remained of former Athens and their circuit was widened to embrace a greater future.

The populace, thronged in the Agora, were negligent, bare-footed, and garbed in dark workaday chitons girdled with leather belts. But the priest, having concluded his announcement, kept his right hand outstretched for a long while before this gathering which resembled a multitude of slaves, as though he stood before an assembly composed solely of kings. Meanwhile he listened to the busy drone of the city as if in it he heard the quivering note of the hammers of destiny.

From the citizens, he who before the gods and the authorities of Athens was the proxenos of Elis, the plenipotentiary representative of Olympian affairs,

approached the spondophoros, offering him his hand
to lead him to the prytaneion.

This was a hastily erected structure, such as a city
destroyed by the Persian conflagration might achieve.
Within it there burned a flame: Hestia's eternal fire.
Into its empty hall, wellnigh dark, stepped the prytanes,
a few archons, and numerous members of the Council.
The Olympian envoy produced from the folds of his
robe a golden bowl and drew wine from a nearby jug.
The king-archon received the vessel and emptied it over
the blazing hearth. Thereupon another archon, one of
the prytanes, the proxenos, and again the spondophoros
himself, each filled the bowl with wine and poured it
over the hearth until the flame was quenched—to re-
kindle after a moment with fresh vigour from the
crackling logs. In the presence of Hestia, for ever hidden
in her fire, in the presence of Zeus, lord of Olympia,
in the presence of Pallas, patroness of the city, Athens
entered into the sacred covenant concluded at the dim
dawn of history by the kings of Elis, Pisa and Sparta.

Meanwhile, in the Agora, memories of the last Olympiad began to mount in men's hearts.

It had taken place at the time when Xerxes crossed
the frontiers of Greece—480 B.C. From Sparta and
Athens despondent embassies had gone forth for succour,
summoning the peoples to a common defence, while the
horizon glowed with fire. But, hedged off from the war
by its mountains and seas, two-thirds of the Grecian
world had secured itself by an alliance with the Persian
king and some states had even dispatched competitors
and processions to Olympia as in the times of undisturbed
peace. On the same day when Thermopylae had been

forced, and at the very moment when in that place Leonidas's naked corpse was being fastened to the cross, athletes were winning the garland in Olympia. The smoke of smouldering Athens must have commingled, perhaps somewhere in the heights of the heavens, with the smoke of the Olympic hecatomb.

These poignant recollections were passed around in an undertone and in broken sentences. Here and there a more impassioned word accused human disloyalty. The Olympian priesthood and the gods were discussed with a bitterness bordering on blasphemy. Moments of silence followed when heads dropped despairingly for the irredeemable sins of times gone by.

Suddenly someone voiced the notion that perhaps Salamis was actually the reward for not having neglected the great festival. The thought was new but involved; nobody probed it, for its cheerful exterior arrested them all.

In the very word "Salamis" there was a captivating charm. It seemed to radiate a glow, everyone felt his cheeks flush, and all breathed freely as though inhaling a celestial ether. The appreciation of victory, which had intensified with each day through the last four years, acted like wine, infusing defiance and courage. In the midst of the most rigorous toil, under the weight of stones for some new building, or over a fresh furrow of a trampled field, there had happened that which occurred at this moment: men stopped suddenly as if stricken with rapture, they burst out laughing, shouted and danced around, many lifted up an almost painful chant like a wail, unexpressed passion swelled every fibre within them, they would have liked to eat and drink,

13

to wrestle on the sand with their bodies naked; the world appeared to be no larger than the stadium, and it seemed that the earth could be hurled like a discus along the Milky Way.

When the spondophoros emerged from the prytaneion, he was astounded to behold a noisy and excited throng— the same that had accorded him a reception of such grave silence.

"By Athena!" said the proxenos. "It will be an Olympiad such as has never been ere now! We are living in great times."

"I am afraid," demurred the priest, "that many will not come. On Thebes and Thessaly one cannot rely."

"The traitors will remain at home, that is certain. Will you be visiting them?"

The spondophoros glanced at him in astonishment.

"Of course! Before Zeus all are equal. The god cares not about our disputes."

Having received refreshment in the house of the proxenos, the spondophoros set out again about noon. He drove in a cart drawn by mules. His tall heraldic staff, thrust into the hay which filled the box of the cart, opened a passage for him through the throng which had assembled on the suburban highway. The north of Greece, Boeotia, Phokis, Euboea, and Thessaly, awaited him. From thence a ship was to bear him along the Thracian shore to Byzantium, where his mission would come to an end.

At the same time the inhabitants of the eastern and western towns would be addressed by two other spondophoroi. These divine ambassadors, elected from noble Elean stock, were to bind into a common union a great amphictyony round the sacred grove. One of them, journeying through Achaia, Aetolia, and Epeiros, would land in Sicily, and after a long journey through the rich towns of Great Greece, he would visit those dwelling on the boundaries of the world: the people of Massalia and Gades. The second, whose itinerary led through Messenia and Laconia, would steer his ship between the isles of the Ægæan Sea and among the harbours of Asia Minor.

From the great tracks along which the spondophoroi roamed, roads, byways, and paths branched out into the heart of the country, and their message was carried onward by word passed from mouth to mouth. It reached the fishermen as they bent over their nets, as though a sudden wave had lifted the boats anchored at the quays. Herdsmen dreamed of it in their pastures. Caravans heard of it one evening in their desert camps. Strangers greeted each other with the announcement. It was talked about in the vineyards and fields, and was the topic in every home.

The palestras and gymnasiums, as many as there were throughout the entire extent of the Greek world, perhaps a thousand, perhaps more, began to stir. Who shall go? To whom can the honour of the town be entrusted? When should the start be made? To these questions there were a hundred answers. As discussion progressed the items became more involved, the elder folk raising doubts. In the case of the outlying districts what mattered most was the expense of the long journey, while elsewhere all depended on the state authorities. Painful anxiety was stilled with promises and hopes. After the exercises, at nightfall, nobody ventured to leave the stadium, and the throng of youths lingered amid passionate whisperings with their eyes fixed on the stars, as though from their gleaming silence was to come the answer deciding their fate.

Here and there, however, there would be found one so independent and so determined that he would start on his own initiative immediately after the spondophoros's announcements. On the way he would meet others, and somewhere about Megara a fairly large party had already formed.

This was a light-hearted band all in white, a small cloudlet on the road moving above the azure of the Corinthian gulf. Without bags, bundles or wains, they tramped freely, their sturdy legs not reckoning distances, carefree lips slaked by cool brooks or taking refreshment from hospitable hands as chance permitted. They travelled along in the incomparable comfort of their youthful years, trusting for a night's lodging to the moss of the woods that had been warmed by the springtide. Several dawns broke over the mountains, and dusks darkened the sea; none were aware of their number—five or six at the most—and one afternoon or another, Elis, with no city wall confining it, drew them in like an eager breath.

CHAPTER II

THE land of Elis occupied the western portion of the Peloponnesus, open to the Ionian Sea by three gulfs with flat and lifeless banks.

No port disturbed by its bustle the quietness seemingly woven of fishing nets. Only in the north Hyrmine and Cyllene kept in the crumbling mainland two roadsteads where, in the last resort, ships from the Ionian Islands, Sicily and the Far West could cast anchor. The sea had pushed Elis back from its routes. The current coming from the Adriatic along Epeiros met with the tide of Patras Gulf and all the sand which it brought, together with the thick ooze that floated out of the mouth of the Achelos—the great river of Aetolia—through centuries had been thrown upon this rim of the Peloponnesus until it was totally blocked and reduced to swamps and lagoons.

On it settled the stubborn fisherfolk who, emaciated through disease amidst the inexhaustible wealth of their hauls, were helpless against the plague of preying insects, the fight with whom they entrusted to the gods. The chapels of Zeus Apomyios—averter of flies—hung all over with votive offerings, were full of crude illustrations depicting miraculous conquests over the assaults of insects. The sea waves swept up to the small temples of Poseidon which were nearly always closed.

Behind this gloomy stretch of lagoons and sands there spread out a wonderful territory sheltered as if by design from the furtive glances of the sea. The plain was wrinkled by slight eminences, which eastward climbed higher and higher, until on the horizon they finally joined the Arcadian mountains in a solid haze. There somewhere, among the ravines of Erymanthos, the Peneios took its source and emerged from the narrow defiles. In the centre of the country it received the tributary Ladon and by the swollen streams a fertilising moisture was distributed on all sides.

Along the banks of these rivers and fed by a hundred brooks and streams lay the valleys, filled with the rustle of the corn which grew up to the slopes of the hillocks. All varieties of trees, from the white poplar that came from the unknown north to the palm grown on some halt of the Phoenician corsair, discovered here a soil and air suitable to their roots and texture. The low ranges smelled of pinewoods. Byssos, a wonderful cotton shrub, found only in this part of Greece, ripened out into pale yellow threads. The ever-present abundance of the cattle, horses and mules has survived in the myth of the stables of Augeas. The delight of the vine was so manifest that the Eleans' faith assigned to this place the ancestry and cradle of Dionysos.

Into this region of tranquillity and plenty, of green valleys and smooth heights, one entered as into a dream of the Golden Age. Nowhere did one meet walls, no fortresses or castles imprisoned the view. There were no quarries, so clay and bricks baked by the sun were used for building. The diminutive dwellings, whitewashed with lime and enlivened by coloured friezes over the doors, were shining spots in the midst of scattered oaks, in the vineyards and orchards. At times they huddled together to form a village, but more commonly they spread out over the fields, caring nothing for the proximity of roads, isolated on paths so narrow as to be scarcely visible. A true calm reigned over this land; at the sight of strangers the inhabitants would straighten from their occupation and shade their eyes with their palms, as time, unheeded, flitted above their unhurried toil. Everything here seemed more buoyant than anywhere else; the breath, the tread, the gravity attached to their pursuits—the work must have been less laborious on these fields where the corn had already begun to wave in the breeze, while in other districts of Greece it was only just starting to sprout.

Along the roads ran a line of columns bearing effigies of Hermes; in the groves and woods were small temples of Aphrodite and Artemis; at every spring there stood a chapel or a cave of the Nymphs; the trees touching at their tops exchanged the offerings hung upon their branches. Those who came from districts which had scarcely healed after the recent war sighed, filling their lungs with the air of a land which, one might say, lay sheltered under divine wings.

This blissful serenity, which seemed a gift of heaven's favour, was in reality acquired by force and bloodshed.

At the southern frontiers of Elis lay Olympia, the object of perpetual contention. Once it had been the possession of Pisa, a small state stretching in a narrow strip along the lower reaches of the Alpheios. As long as the Olympian grove was the shrine of a few neighbouring communities no one's envy urged the capture of this silent and modest region. After the harvests ceremonies and feasts were held, prayers were offered to the old deities: Earth, Kronos and Mother Rhea secreting her child in a mountain cave. On certain days Games were arranged at which the kings of Pisa judged the competitors' performances and presented rewards. But with time the Games became famous, the sanctity of the site spread its rays farther and farther afield and the first temple, Hera's, was erected by the town of Skillus.

Prolonged and crafty contention resulted, the king of Pisa was obliged to cede half of his sway over Olympia to the king of Elis, and both presided at the Games. Pisa found opposition futile, for behind Elis stood Sparta. It was then that the sacred alliance was effected which established the truce of the gods, a season of Games every fourth year and the rights for competitors. The three kings of Elis, Pisa and Sparta avowed eternal alliance, and the solemn pledge was carved upon a bronze discus and placed in the Heraeon in the custody of the goddess. Aristotle saw this ancient disc on which, through the patina, could still be read the name of the Spartan Lycurgos.

Through some centuries peace prevailed. Elis, indeed, acquired increasing might, but, as before, the two allied kings presided over the Olympic stadium. Later, there were no kings; both states simultaneously changed their form of government, and the supreme authority passed into the hands of the oligarchy of powerful families. The management of the Games was entrusted to two dignitaries known as hellanodikai. These were always descendants of an old line, heirs to the legends and heroes, and were garbed during the festivals in royal purple. Weakened Pisa in all this had only a dwindling share; bitterness increased within her and hasty, ill-considered altercation led to war. Elis crushed the Pisans, and their ancient capital, situated on rising ground a few stades off from Olympia, perished by fire and little by little faded away, even to its name.

The new enlarged Elean state was conveniently placed in the valleys of the three rivers Peneios, Ladon and Alpheios. It did not experience any shocks, it did not interfere in the affairs of others, over its fertile fields there did not pass even that thirst for adventure which drove settlers out from all other parts of Greece to colonies overseas. It seemed that the history of this country had fallen asleep in the shadow of the Olympic olive.

It was awakened only by the rumble of the Persian war. The oligarchy then governing did not take up the watchword of national defence. It intended to wait so that at the last moment it could take sides with the conquerors, as was the custom of the theocracies and aristocratic governments. They judged so well that at the moment when fighting had ceased the Elean contingent had just reached Plataeae. The victorious Greeks were on the point of burning offerings and dividing out the spoil. The tardy allies were laughed at, theirs was a disgrace in the eyes of the whole world. The Elean armies returned home with a feeling of shame and treachery. The democratic party took advantage of this mood, they dominated perturbed minds and brought about a revolution. After the overthrow of the oligarchy there arose a confederation of communities, officials were elected, all decisions were made by the Council of the Six

Hundred, and assemblies of the people were held as in Athens.

But this did not change the life of the country; it was not to be disturbed from its rural serenity. The people lolled in the vineyards and fields, not caring for governments, nor heeding much their capital, which took on an importance only in the Olympic year, for it was here that the administration of the Games was situated. This management also underwent a change. Instead of two hereditary hellanodikai, nine were elected, one from each Elean tribe. Their tenure of office extended over four years and terminated a month after the end of the Games.

This year it was the first Olympiad of the new hellanodikai. They were elected from among those citizens to whom affluence gave freedom and independence. The affairs of gymnastics and competitors were strange to nobody; the hellanodikai, however, distinguished themselves by a greater knowledge than the rest. In spite of this, they were not trusted to such an extent that they were left without the tutelage of experience and tradition. Hence, the two previous hellanodikai were retained to assist them with their counsels. They did not wield any authority, their personal decisions did not determine anything, but, for these two veterans whose life had been spent amidst the Games and who did not comprehend a world outside the stadium, it was sufficient consolation that in their new dignity of "guardians of the law"— nomophylakes, as they were called—they could preserve the wisdom of ages amid the chaos of the new and unruly times.

CHAPTER III

E LIS, the capital of the Elean territory, was situated in the heart of the country on the Peneios. Spread out like a village, it hid its little brick houses amongst gardens and groves. In those parts of the city where the tenements were packed closer, the interest centred on gymnastic activities, trade and industry. Through the open doors could be seen the artisans manufacturing discs, spears, dumb-bells for leaping, leather straps for boxing, scrapers. Shops selling olive-oil formed a long line tailing off amongst the potters' stalls. The street was over-stocked with all kinds of oil vessels, from tiny aryballoi and bombylioi to the large double-eared amphores suffi-cient to hold many months' supply. Usually in this vicinity the older athletes paraded about or sat on benches, anticipating orders for their services as trainers. They snatched at chances for conversation with the young people, staggering them by their knowledge of the varieties of olive-oil and their judgment of gymnastic equipment.

But the aspirants who arrived that day found the houses shut, the streets empty, nobody about from whom the way to the gymnasium could be inquired. They located it unassisted, recognising the spacious area circled by a wall. They did not, however, find the nearest

23

gate, which was approached by the road leading to the river through the Street of Silence, but tramped around till they arrived at the Agora. There they found themselves unexpectedly in the midst of an excited crowd.

The whole Agora buzzed with strange whispering and murmurs. Suddenly all became quiet and from the western side singing was heard.

In this part of the Agora stood the temple of Seilenos and behind it a smaller structure devoid of ornaments, columnless and topped by a flat roof. Its four-cornered shape resembled that of a stone die. The low bronze door, green with verdigris, was closed, and the bar with which it was bolted was bound round with a heavily knotted cord. Immediately before this sealed door a band of sixteen priestesses was singing:

> Come in springtime, Dionysos,
> To thy holy shrine in Elis,
> With the Graces to thy temple;
> Haste on foot of bull towards us,
> Noble Bull! O noble Bull!

The refrain was repeated over and over again, with increasing tempo and swelling passion; it was already at an ear-piercing pitch when abruptly it ceased. The crowd became motionless, and all gazed fixedly at the door of the chapel.

The priestesses unfastened the rope, each in turn undoing one knot. The last one drew the bolt and three of them passed into the interior. The hush in the Agora became heavier and deeper. Shortly the three women reappeared on the threshold carrying a heavy pitcher. The joy which beamed from their countenances spread like the rays of the sun. Shouts burst out in praise of Dionysos.

One of the Eleans said to the newcomers:

"This is our Dionysian Festival, the Thyia. And this is our miracle of wine. Every year in the sealed temple three empty pitchers fill themselves with wine. Euoe!"

And so saying, he ran to satisfy himself and see the pitchers of fruitfulness with his own eyes.

The new arrivals with difficulty made their way through the throng to reach the portico, which, situated at the other end of the Agora, was the entrance to the gymnasium. Beside it was the house of the hellanodikai, the judges and managers of the Games. The young competitors entered. After a while one of the hellanodikai appeared and while the sun was setting he wrote down their names. Each one gave the name of his father and the name of the community to which he belonged.

One of the "guardians of the law", a grey-haired veteran, listened attentively to this rite, every now and then interrupting with a question or a warning that only the truth was required. The hellanodikai, on whose script the dusk was settling, grew impatient. But the old man continued to repeat:

"Remember, only pure Hellenic blood and hands unstained by crime have a right to the revered competitions. Your names, your descent, your life will be re-examined, we will procure the verification of witnesses, people from your own communities, and the deceiver will incur the wrath of the gods."

After this they were quartered in the dormitory attached to the gymnasium. Each one was allotted no more than a bed, narrow and hard and bare. In the chamber provided, movement was limited to a minimum, this mattered little to them, as the short night was solely for rest, and with the grey dawn all would be already in the stadium.

The Olympic law prescribed that the month before the Games should be spent by all participants in training in Elis. As a rule, however, competitors arrived earlier and for an obol a day they availed themselves of the perfect arrangements of the gymnasium. There were others who spent the whole ten months training according to the rules, the impecunious ones by the charity of their communities.

Those of more mature experience issued forth naked from the night-lodge to the surprise of the newcomers. This they did, not because they followed settled custom but because they knew there were no cloak-rooms here as there were in other gymnasiums. Anyone taking off his chiton tossed it on one arm and then on the other, having nowhere to put it. Some returned to their lodgings, others determinedly left their chitons folded on the turf near the wall.

The experienced athletes scrutinised the new arrivals closely. Legs, shoulders, the trunk betrayed individuality like unmasked faces, they exhibited candidly the exact proportions of the man, his intentions and possibilities. Each of the newcomers felt that his body was a focus for eyes which measured, examined and felt him. It almost hurt when some detecting eye found a rumple of fat or a muscle underdeveloped. Some of their number did not fail to hear such phrases as:

"Never mind, you will soon be rid of that soft pad there."

The newcomers' distrust of the older set and the coarse liberties indulged in by the latter were bridged over by such questions as: "What's your name?" "Where from?" "What are you going in for?"

The boys answered promptly in subdued tones; they stood motionless, with eyelids lowered, unable to overcome a slight shiver prompted by the approach of a strange man. The older hands forthwith became talkative and more noisy than was necessary. Almost every second one—if his own version were believed—had far outclassed his co-aspirants during the Games of the different festivals; it was but a pace that separated the narrator from the Pythian laurel; only an unfair fate had snatched the crowning success from him at the Isthmus or Nemea. Frequently they exclaimed: "This Elis of yours!" casting at the track a deprecating glance, as if even the stadium was too short for them. Every account concluded with the deliberate: "we at Corinth", "we at Athens", "we at Ægina", until someone exceeded the magniloquence by exclaiming "we at Opous"!

"Oh, and what of Opous, tell us?" softly inquired Sodamos from Miletos.

The Opountian Epharmostos, a sturdy muscular youth, was taken aback at the ensuing silence which was as the void of a desert. His face reddened:

"At Opous," he stuttered, "the gymnasium is in the woods."

"By Artemis, that is very sensible! You can revel in chasing hares."

There followed a chorus of guffaws and all eyes turned to peer at the stranger who had thus spoken.

No one knew him, he had not spent the night at the

gymnasium; where he came from that morning no one could tell; dusky streaks still showed in circles above his feet, from which he was removing his sandals. But at first sight all were decided in their opinion of him.

It is he, the life of the stadium, the comrade and friend of everyone; he is the one to whom the hellanodikai are lenient; he is ever fresh and prepared to undertake all exercises, each defeat increasing his determination to improve his form.

A veritable pentathlon contestant, his body was like the polished grain threshed clear of straw and chaff. With his eighteen years he stood on the borderline between grace and strength; the side on which he should be counted still hung in the balance: ought he to be allotted to the boys or to the men? His name was Sotion, he came from Tarentum, his paternal uncle brought him over in his ship, and only the day before yesterday it had berthed at Patrai.

"I had no idea which road led to Elis," quoth he; one was inclined to believe that some bird had shown him the way.

"I imagined that I should meet a bigger gathering here." At a single glance he took in the thirty pairs of eyes bestowing on him their sympathy.

"You ought to have come along with me," began Sodamos.

He was the first arrival here. His elder brother, with whom he was in business, had brought him over in the autumn before the winter storms set in; by now he would be sailing somewhere along the African coast. Sodamos had been, during this time, the sole foreigner among the Eleans. Rains had deluged the stadium so much that he fell a-dreaming of a jug of wine beside a hearth in which a fire devoured the dry logs hewn in the summer.

"I was next-door to senility. Then came these Arcadians, from whom you never heard a word."

He pointed to two youths, a few paces apart from the others.

The prepuce was fastened with narrow ties which were allowed to hang loosely or lifted up and tucked in under the girdle round the hips. Each one had his own method of fastening, explaining its merits with reference to health and even to elegance.

"Could anyone lend me a little olive-oil?" asked Sotion. "I forgot to bring it with me."

"Here's some, help yourself," they offered from all sides. If he had wished, he could have bathed in the quantity handed to him. The Athenian Gryllos stood nearest, so Sotion accepted from him a small aryballos, a tiny earthen vessel globular in shape, having a narrow vent, through which the thick fluid trickled in green drops.

The entire body, from the ankles to the rim of the hair on the head, was massaged with it. The competitors assisted each other in turn. Some of them had the service of slaves or of retired athletes whom they employed as trainers. The latter were called aleiptai, masseurs, and their skill was admired. He who came through their hands was of a rosy tint all over as if, you would say, he had bathed in the dawn. The youths always requisitioned their services if their means permitted it, for in them they also had tutors; but rich Xenophon of Corinth was surrounded by a retinue of servants. Those from Sparta viewed this with disdain.

Their law forbade them teachers and assistants. They were accustomed to reckon solely on themselves; with a rare skill they rubbed themselves unassisted; some of them seemed as if caught by a whirlpool, capering wildly, with their bodies spinning at speed and bending on all sides amid clapping hands, puffing and blowing.

One of them, flinging aside an empty aryballos, leaped up:

"Praise to my tribe!" he exclaimed. "We were the first users of the divine oil of the olive. We originated gymnastics."

Sodamos looked at him over his shoulder:

"Your name is Eutelidas and if you were deprived of your name you would not weigh more than your silly words."

Everyone grinned. Eutelidas, offended by the slander on his name, which was supposed to be inherited from a famous Olympic victor, shouted:

"You have perpetually a pair of scales and a yardstick to hand, you shopkeeper!"

Sodamos did not deny his mercantile calling.

"Should pirates ever bring you as far as Miletos, I shall buy you for a few drachmæ."

The Spartan was at a loss for a reply. In the meantime, however, they started to fling at him whatever they could in the shape of jokes and insults. They shouted him down. It was only Gryllos who switched back to the start:

"What do you mean by 'we'? You certainly are not serious when you say the Spartans invented gymnastics?"

"No, I said the Dorians."

"That's better, but it is also untrue. Have you heard of Homer?"

General laughter broke out again, for who could be asked such a question otherwise than as a joke?

Eutelidas replied:

"What has Homer to do with it?"

"As usual, very much. But first tell me: do you think Homer was a Dorian?"

Someone remarked:

"He may have been, for they say he was from Argos."

Such a howling burst out that it seemed that all the towns in which Homer was supposed to have been born were taking part in the quarrel. But Gryllos, young, marked with the first sprouts of adolescent hair, subdued the uproar with his sensible composure:

"But you will not find even a single sound of Doric in Homer. He uses our old Ionic language and a little of the Æolic dialect."

Besides Eutelidas, only the thick-headed Bœotian Pataikos from Thespiae failed to see the point. Homer was certainly the first to mention Games, he knew all the contests, but he was no Dorian. . . . Surely it's as clear as the day? By Zeus, it is certain that the Dorians did not invent gymnastics! "Wonderful, Gryllos, wonderful!" "You have convinced us very well indeed." "Don't join in the boxing. It would be a shame were someone to smash your skull to pieces!" "Seemingly you have already defeated us!" Patting him on the back and ruffling his hair, they were overjoyed by the skilfully convincing argument of the two questions and a few sentences discharged, as it were, like arrows and hanging silently in space.

Gryllos went nearer to Eutelidas:

"And this too I will add: you Spartans are of no importance in gymnastics. A hundred years ago you occupied the first place everywhere, but the smallest country now has more victors than your great Sparta. You are at the same stage as you were in the olden times and will never advance any further. The ephors permit you to cultivate neither boxing nor the pancration. Why? For they know you would accomplish nothing, everyone would defeat you. They left you only vulgar scuffling. Perhaps you are worth something, but of a certainty not so much as your ancestor and namesake, the beautiful Eutelidas, who alone, out of all the youths, won the pentathlon."

Gryllos poured this forth in an exceptional passion. Eutelidas darkened with anger:

"Of no importance? By the Dioskouroi," he yelled, "you will soon be convinced! You do well to enter for the hoplite-race; practise, practise running in armour, so that you may outrun my spear."

Facing each other threateningly, as if they were about to hurl themselves at their opponents, challenges were bawled out which nobody could follow. Confusion was on all sides, many were stirred up by this eruption of hatred. Some took the side of Athens, others of Sparta. Though few in number, they represented the stormy diversity of the Grecian world; a hundred times a day they quarrelled about things that had estranged their ancestors through generations, ridiculing each other's dialects and habits, setting at naught each other's gods and heroes. In such moments conflicts arose, continuing the unfinished disputes in the histories of their towns, while above their frenzy there clanged the swords of an impending war.

Sotion stood apart with folded arms. For the first time in his life he was in Hellas, and if the few days spent on the way from Patrai to Elis were not counted, the morning of this day could be reckoned as his first on the old soil. Remote and aloof, his thoughts inclined towards his native town which suddenly appeared before him like a mirage in the desert.

In a semi-circle of hills Tarentum spreads its streets fanwise, with their convergence at the harbour. The protruding peninsula cuts this off from the great sea which flows in through only a narrow strait. Thousands of boats sail around, their occupants bending over the sides and drawing in the nets laden with fish. Elsewhere stakes driven into the bottom of the bay indicate the whereabouts of the purple mussels. Near the dams are vessels with furled sails, and Sotion, born a disc's throw from the port, pictures himself counting masts, while from the signs on their prows—the griffons, birds, deities, sphinxes—he guesses the countries they hail from. And yonder is the rivulet Galesos, dark among the yellow fields. At its first bend outside the town is the tombstone of Phalanthos, the founder of Tarentum.

Sotion had never been clear about the story recounting the first Messenian war: some conspiracy; the loss of everything because Phalanthos had not donned his helmet, which was to have been the agreed sign; when people had thrown themselves into the temple and at the altars imploring mercy, while others again were fleeing the country; when women, though they had children, were always called "virgins"—all this mingled in a nightmare of outrage and misfortune, but one detail stood out from this confusion: the ship, which after a dreadful tempest, half shattered, drifts into the blessed strait, and Phalanthos, leaping ashore, kisses the soil and takes it for his own.

Phalanthos was descended from the Heracleidae, his followers were all Spartans. In Sotion's veins flowed Spartan blood. But not even a single drop stirred when Gryllos was abusing Eutelidas. Fortified with calmness and indifference, he stood in the vicinity of the quarrel like the living picture of Tarentum, watching from the shelter of its strait the storm which could not reach it. At last he shouted at them, as from the watch-tower of a better world:

"And will you be long at your bickering?"

First to leap off was Sodamos, still flushed after the alliance with the Athenians. Gradually all became quiet and returned to their rubbing—even Eutelidas, who bent down for his aryballos, in which not even a drop was left. Everyone weighed the words that had yet to be expressed. Timasarchos, most unexpectedly, broke the silence. This youth was of a famous family of Aeginetan musicians. The clarity of his voice undoubtedly surpassed his pugilistic abilities. Having no justifiable say in the men's altercation, he remained pondering over the origin of the quarrel and now began to recite that portion of the Iliad in which the poet sings of the Games at the tomb of Patroklos.

Everybody became still, hands ceased rubbing bodies. They listened, with half-shut eyes the sooner, the clearer to see the plain of Troy, the pile of stones which served as the goal, the chariots lined up for the start.

Five heroes held the reins: Antilochos, Diomedes, Menelaus, Eumelos, Merioneus—which meant five regions of Greece (Messenia, Argolis, Laconia, Thessaly, Crete) contesting in the race. And now when they are covered in dust, the listeners' souls are fervent with prayer; each one, longing that victory be for his country, is almost convinced that the lines written centuries before could be reversed. But look, Eumelos falls out of his chariot, Menelaus reins in his horses on the marshy ground, the shrill shout of Antilochos is heard, and in the end the bay stallions of Diomedes drip with the sweat of a hard-fought victory.

After this came the boxing bout in which Epeios covered Euryalos with blood, the undecided wrestling between Aias and Odysseus, the foot-races in which Antilochos was placed last, the spear throwing, the archery and the hurling of the lump of iron which Polypoites threw right out of the field.

In the ancient words were revealed the same Games, the test of skill, strength and determination. A grand pride uplifted their thoughts. They felt that every activity of the stadium of their day had been decided and fixed in the muscles of the heroes before the gods in the golden glory of this myth. Their blood coursed with a hexametric measure. Time slid back: Nestor's tales of the Buprasion races were canopied in rhapsody by the Elean heaven. Buprasion, not far away, barely a day's walk, seemed nearer. Everything became near. Troy, to them, seemed to be squatting on the hill above the town. The gymnasium was the bivouac of the Greeks. Peneios, behind the walls, flowed with the roar of the Skamandros. A delightful anxiety forbade them to look

35

round. A shiver like to the breath of a mysterious presence ran down their backs: had Achilles perhaps suddenly risen from his grave which lay at the entrance to the gymnasium?

Then someone at the back cried out. It was Hysmon, one of the hellanodikai, come to start the day's exercises.

CHAPTER IV

ON THE SACRED TRACK

THE competitors passed on to the "sacred track", as that part of the gymnasium was called that was intended for the sprints, the discus and spear-throwing and the leaps. It had a rectangular shape. The rows of plane-trees bordering the four sides made small patches of shade which danced on the sunny sand. The start was marked out at one edge of the rectangle by a distinct grooved line, and a similar line at the opposite end, between two wooden posts, was the position of the goal. Closing in the length of the stadium on the remaining sides were two other lines, six hundred Olympic feet, a measure fixed of old by the length of Heracles's foot.

A slave brought a long forked rod and gave it to the hellanodikes. Hysmon summoned the new arrivals, ordering them to divide off into boys and men. A certain amount of confusion arose, as they had different ideas of age. In many regions the "beardless" were distinguished from both boys and men; Sotion belonged properly to these. Glaukos of Chios knew not which way to turn. In his island the ages of competitors were sorted into five categories, but in Olympia those from fifteen to eighteen years of age were classed as boys. So Sotion was assigned to the men and Glaukos to the boys. In point of fact, it was the bodily dimensions, the physical maturity, that guided Hysmon in his decisions rather than dates for which no fixed chronology existed.

The first quartet of boys was selected. At the starting point Hysmon scrutinised their stances. The legs had to be kept together with the right foot placed behind, and its big toe touching the side of the left heel, the knees had to be slightly flexed and the trunk bent a little forward.

"Hold the head upright, extend the right arm as in greeting."

The eyes of the hellanodikai with the exactness of a pair of compasses measured angles and incorrect postures, while checked impatience added increasing fatigue to the runners' muscles. They grew old with waiting and lost hope of ever reaching the goal.

At last the roar, "Apite—Go!" rent the silence like a thunderclap.

Only a few paces were covered. Swish! went the rod across someone's flanks, and all were ordered back. Wheeling round at the height of their speed, they returned like a gushing torrent, in a daze. What had happened no one knew.

They had started too fast. Before they had learnt to tell from their breathing the point at which to begin running freely, the command was given by the hellanodikai for two fresh pairs of runners. Some of the sprints were completed, but Hysmon was not satisfied. He admonished some for not keeping a straight course but swerving either to the right or to the left, thereby losing energy in unnecessary exertion. Of others he had remarked that their stride was too long at the start. Two or three, by their lack of perseverance, betrayed a neglected training.

From the deathlike livid parted lips one could see the exhausting effort expended; hands were pressed against thumping hearts. Poor Timasarchos, who had to cover the length of the course twice over, because of the hellanodikes's inattention, reeled in the last stride at the goal. But he ran on to the wall where faintness overcame him and, with hands falling limp, sank down on the stones vomiting. Melesias, his trainer, assisted by Sotion, carried him onto the turf.

Hysmon next chose quartets from among the men, and Sotion was included in the first set. They practised the diaulos: this was a sprint to the goal and back again to the start. The various steps—halting at the goal, turning about, and posing in the same attitude as at the start—seemed beyond human endurance. One would retard his pace too early in his anxiety not to run past the goal, another would turn about so sharply that in doing so he would tumble on his neighbour, and all were too excited to reproduce the correct starting posture.

The "initiated" looked on, grinning at the "newer set" in their despairing endurance of the rigid Olympic rules. Each one had undergone similar experiences when it had seemed he was totally ignorant, that he was fit for nothing, that this was the first appearance in his life on a stadium, and when in the end he had collapsed unable to carry out any further orders, the swish of the rod had only increased his panic.

Gryllos returned from his race out of breath but full of enthusiasm:

"By Athena," he gasped, "that is good work! In our town, since the war, there have been no decent gymnasiums."

39

"But it is said that in Athens are the best teachers," argued Sodamos also in an undertone.

"Say: there were. All have now gone to Ægina, where they are paid with heavy gold. There—do you see Melesias massaging his pupil? A year ago he was still in Athens."

The parley ceased when Hysmon's voice rang out. The hellanodikes was remonstrating with one of the sprinters. He lectured: Mere speed is not sufficient, animals possess it in a high degree, certainly no man is a match for a stag. But man alone is capable of developing such action to the point where it becomes an artistic performance. He ought at every moment to be so balanced that, were he suddenly to change into stone, he would reveal in that transformed figure all the beauty of pose, movement and relaxation of the features.

Still further varieties of races over longer distances were tried out until fully noon. The posts at the goal were removed by the slaves and in the centre a stone base was placed. The track now lay round this. Seven and twelve laps had to be run. The boys did not take part in these courses, and many of the men dropped out from fatigue.

Over the longest distance the best performer was Ergoteles. Sodamos was astonished:

"You said you were from Himera? Indeed, I never saw a Sicilian before who ran so well."

"I am only a recent citizen of Himera. I was born in Crete."

"That is immediately obvious," affirmed Sodamos. "On that island the best runners are born."

Others, however, inquired what had driven him away

from the country. Ergoteles recounted the circumstances unwillingly. There had been brawls and fights between factions in which his father, Philanor, had been killed. He was listened to with sympathy. It's a cruel occasion when a man is torn away from his soil; when he leaves behind him the ashes of his fathers, the protection of his gods, a whole world of things which can never again be recovered. Ergoteles continued: "I would like to win the wreath as a consolation to the soul of my poor father." This set them musing: Was it possible that Philanor's soul could abandon the grave, fly over the sea and come to shelter in a strange abode in order to touch the wreath of his son? Would the Sicilian deities permit its entry? They remained silent, gazing beyond him as if into a distant blurred emptiness spread over the horizon.

He did not guess their thoughts; obviously he had made up his mind on these problems long since. Gratified that he was commanding so much of their attention and even surmising that their silence was an acknowledgment of his inmost thoughts, he began to tell of his journey and plans. After the Olympiad he intended visiting the various local Games. In the gymnasium and on his way he calculated that he would make acquaintances who would assure him protection in the foreign regions. "Of course," "Undoubtedly," he was assured. Still absorbed in their musing, none of them were able to say more. From the moment that Ergoteles had changed for them from a Sicilian into a Cretan, every concern of his was worthy of their consideration.

His complexion swarthier than the southern sun accounted for, the slightly hooked nose, the unusual slimness of his limbs in spite of their fine muscles, his enviable stature, and besides the mysterious existence of something in the eyes (or was it something in the mouth?) an intangible entity as if separate from the figure but hovering somewhere in the atmosphere surrounding it—all this did not exactly estrange the others but intervened like a faint shadow between him and the comrades who were listening to him. They wondered when the Cretan called out: *Akara*, meaning his feet; when he exclaimed: *Droion!* on beholding anything beautiful. When he parted his straight lips to emit these foreign expressions, all stared silently at him—it seemed as though a crevice had opened, revealing unknown and mysterious things.

This moment at dusk truly concealed within itself the great night of the Past. There were in it palaces, towns, centuries of work and power; the wiry, narrow-hipped, supple tribe of an unknown origin and language that had appeared from somewhere up the steps of civilisation, of stone, copper and bronze, that had built and created, had enlightened the whole Ægean archipelago, had sailed the Mediterranean Sea up to the ports of Egypt, had possessed its wealth and its art, had related its history on thin earthen tablets, had danced and sung and played on the harp, had fought bulls in the arena, had organised Games, planted the olive-seed and the vine-slip, they had been the subjects of kings whose emblem was the lily—until there had come the day of destruction when everything was swallowed up, disappearing under the earth as if all had been but a magic illusion.

The Cretan Ergoteles, by birth from Knossos, stood as

on the dizziest height of his forgotten inheritance—his every fibre and whole soul reflecting this in his attitude —and all the while on the same spot, where till recently his father's house had stood, on the range of hills that loomed above the palace (now razed to the ground) of the kings of his tribe. But he was not conscious of this reverie, and neither did any of those gazing at him in such rapt attention realise that his thoughts were elsewhere. Their racial instinct, like a small faint flame for a moment shorter than a passing thought, had merely kindled in them a shuddering premonition, which then was extinguished as if blown out by Sotion's words:

"If Tarentum happens to be on any of the roads you intend taking, remember you are always welcome as a guest to my house."

The running was finished in the meanwhile and all could depart for the midday repast.

The site of the kitchen could not be located by its smell, for none came from it. The food consisted of cheese and fruit, a handful of olives and slices of bread. Wine was prohibited and vendors were not allowed within the premises of the gymnasium. Having received from the steward their portions wrapped in fig-leaves, the competitors returned to the stadium. Sotion broke his cheese up into pellets and pecked at them with his fingers like a child. He was the longest eating. For the end he reserved two dried figs and when he came to these he nibbled at them, biting off minute morsels. As he never had his mouth full, he could talk without pausing. He narrated the legends of all the palestras and gymnasiums, about men that ran faster than horses, about hunters who caught up with the stag.

"Pheidippides ran from Athens to Sparta in two days," announced Eutelidas.

"And still had time to talk with the gods on his way," added Gryllos.

"How was that—to talk with the gods?" questioned Sotion.

"Really? Have you not heard of it?"

"No, not a word."

"When the herald Pheidippides was running on the mission from the Athenian leaders, Pan crossed his path. He looked just as they represent him: bearded and with goat's legs and feet. Pheidippides was terrified, but Pan greeted him warmly and complained that the Athenians neglected him in spite of his kindness to them. He had already done so much good for them and intended still to help them at need. These Arcadians, if they had tongues in their mouths, would tell you that that is true, because it was supposed to have occurred in their districts in the Parthenios mountains close to Tegea."

All eyes turned to gaze at the two Arcadians sitting motionless as if really human speech was unintelligible to them. Gryllos again turned to Sotion:

"When Pheidippides related this occurrence in Athens, a small temple was promptly carved out for Pan in the rock at the foot of the Acropolis, and since then yearly sacrifices are made there to him on that day."

"How many stades would it be from Athens to Sparta?" inquired Sodamos.

"One thousand one hundred and sixty," supplied Eutelidas.

44

"Phew! to cover that within two days! It would be difficult now to find such runners."

"And what about Euchidas?" came as a sudden interrogation from Pataikos.

"Of course, Euchidas," assented Gryllos. "He was a great runner. He was the one sent from Plataeae to Delphi to fetch a fresh fire, for you know," he said to Sotion, "at that time all the fires had been desecrated by the Persians and so a fresh fire had to be got from the Delphian temple; well, he ran there and returned the same day."

"I know that road," intimated Epharmostos; "there and back it will be about a thousand stades. And what a road! Mountains and mountains only."

Gradually the conversation dwindled. Thighs ached from the running, the hot sun increased their lethargy, the crowing of the cocks could be heard in the distance and made them feel hotter. They leaned their backs against the cool wall and stretched their bodies to relieve stiffness, drowsiness closed their lips on partly uttered words, the warm murmur of the blood stirred up by the exercises spoke to them of goals scented with twigs of wild olive.

They were aroused from their doze by the sound of creaking wheels. The donkey-cart carrying the pot-bellied pithos arrived. It had come, driven by an Elean peasant, from the precincts of Akroreia. At dawn he had started downhill from the mountains, reaching here only at noon. He brought fresh water in his well-stoppered earthen jar and was greeted by a burst of cheers on his arrival. Lifting the cover off the jar and filling a goblet, he handed it first to Sodamos, whom he had known the longest. Each in turn tossed aside a small quantity for the gods before drinking, taking care to do this as skilfully as could be managed in order to spill only the fewest drops.

Water! The blood of the soil, colourless and pure as the ichor flowing in the veins of the gods! Its source an unpenetrated secret, it emerges by way of the gravel and stones, pumped onwards, as it were, by the rhythmical beat of a heart. In a small fold of the gigantic body of Mother Earth dwells a Naiad, resembling a dewdrop on the coarse bark of an oak. Her whole life's toil is given by this particle of divinity to the uninterrupted spinning of the long-drawn liquid thread, a blessed gossamer. And here is the form of this transparent goddess, the coolness of her virgin beauty, the fragrance of her sylvan hair, the taste of her wet lips; contained in this goblet, all her body—alive and immortal, unadulterated and always the same—enters into man.

Having drained the goblet dry, each one held his breath for a moment, as if afraid to frighten away the deity pervading him.

The resting interval was over. A slave, the flute-player, came on the scene and performed on the aulos during the leaps, discus- and spear-throwing. The older athletes knew him and hailed him by name: Smilax. Short and speechless, as if the long chiton patterned with great yellow flowers, which he wore, had smothered and made him dumb, he answered only with a shake of his head. Then were brought the weights for jumping: the *halteres.*

These were for the most part new and made of iron, having been purchased in Elis. They resembled small

46

boats or quarter sections of an apple. They were hollowed out in the centre to afford a better grip. They were undoubtedly handy, useful, and of perfect make. But some entrants possessed older ones—semi-circular sickle-shaped pieces of stone. These, having been long in use, had smoothed into a soft concavity whereon the hands in the middle rested loosely. Some might have been called awkward in shape, yet no one would have thought of parting with such a token. They were inherited from fathers and grandfathers, and the possessors believed that, in addition to their weight assisting the flight of the body throughout a leap, they were reinforced with wings by the souls of their ancestors in their aerial presence. Those who could not boast of such a possession ascribed this lack to wars or conflagrations, or explained how their ancestors had taken them to their graves or had deposited them in a temple in memory of their victories.

Sotion, as an exception, exhibited with pride two cylindrical leaden pieces which blackened the hands wherever touched.

"I was seven years old when my father took these out from the strong-box and gave them to me. In giving them he wept bitterly because they had previously done service for my elder brother, who died."

And Sotion, musing for the second time this day, returned to Tarentum. There is the broad way behind the town, lined with tombstones on both sides. Among them, in the shape of a tall stone slab, rises the stele on which, in bas-relief, a youth with a discus is sculptured. The discus shines with its great white circle beside his head and it seems the brother's smiling face has emerged from the full moon.

47

The hellanodikes arrived. Smilax, putting the flute to his mouth, blew a few notes of the Pythian melody. Hysmon called Sodamos to start the jumping.

Picking up his *halteres* in a firm grasp, Sodamos ran a few short jumping steps and stood on the stone slab: the *bater*. Here with a sudden swing of his arms he brought the *halteres* up to the level of his head and then threw them violently down, bending simultaneously so that his hands reached down below his knees. At the next instant, from this position he swung the *halteres* upwards and leapt into the air, seemingly as if the weight of the *halteres* had wrenched him off the ground. His course through the air was a flattened curve, arched, over his outstretched arms, which at the last minute he jerked back, to force his body still further forward—and then he landed.

The length of the leap was marked by a line drawn on the sand. Hysmon judged it to be about fifteen feet. It was not too bad a beginning, yet it did not predict the true course of events. One after the other went through their leaps following no rule. One would stumble on landing, another would trip over, while some would leap with legs apart, but Sodamos's line until now remained unbeaten. It was equalled only by Sotion, who after a while was ordered by the hellanodikes to repeat his leap.

He did not achieve a greater length, but it was not for this purpose that the repetition was ordered; it was because of his exemplary posture, action and flight.

The few moments taken up by his jump were indistinguishable from the accompanying music. From the first breath of his run he caught its rhythm: the closing of the legs on the leaping-base, the two semi-circles of the arms swinging the *halteres* and the moment of leaving the ground united in a multiform wave with the notes of the aulos. The curve of the jump developed almost into a straight line, and one got the impression that this invisible line was like a stretched cord, fixed to some specific point ahead, drawn close and charmed by the power of the jumper's straining eyes. The final plunge forwards and the backward thrust of the arms were carried through with such nicety of movement that it seemed he was not suspended in the air, that he was not under the power of the transporting impetus but that for this microscopic fraction of time he had found a solid, firm base like the ground, up there in space. And then he was only a weight which fell. He now seemed asleep, his eyes were closed and under the thin lids the convexity of the cornea was prominent. The long eyelashes cast shadows on his cheeks. Having landed, he rebounded lightly and checked himself with all the strength of his strained calves and, as if actually waking from slumber, stretched out his arms and chest, taking in a deep breath.

The hellanodikes inspected him attentively. His eyes, travelling from head to foot, were arrested by the dusty streaks circling his ankles. The competitors who, ready with their *halteres*, awaited their turn drew nearer. They had never seen such a thing before. No one had been the object of special attention from the instructor of exercises, the future judge of the Games. The beatings and chidings had kept them all on an absolute equality. No room had been left for anyone to develop illusions of individual distinction. Meanwhile Hysmon turned to Sotion:

"Did you arrive to-day? From afar?"

"From Buprasion. During the day I rested there and departed at nightfall."

Nothing more was said, but every breast heaved a profound sigh. For these words had their significance. They expressed the true appreciation of an able accomplishment which depended not so much on the gracefulness of the leap as on the patience, the unpretentious courage and absence of self-consciousness in a youth who, having made a lengthy journey, had undertaken two events in the stadium. And even after that his frame had submitted every ounce of the vigour of its thighs to three turns at wielding the *halteres*. They all felt the hot breath of pleasure and pride. To them Sotion appeared enthroned on an uplifted shield which they themselves were supporting by its rim with their own hands.

The jumping had now come to an end and the hellanodikes ordered the discs to be brought.

The throwing base was the *balbis*. This site was marked out by three lines drawn in such a manner that it seemed someone had intended to design a square but had left one side undrawn. It was a narrow space, no broader than two feet. Overstepping the front line, or even treading on it with so much as the toes, meant disqualification. Here the hellanodikes took his stand. Before, however, it came to measuring the length of the throws, the novices had to prove their proficiency in the required posture. Some conducted themselves awkwardly and were dispatched to the end positions, there to correct their faults.

Meanwhile, the older ones were called up. Each one in turn strewed sand over his discus to ensure a surer grip. He then stepped into the *balbis*, executed

the correct movements and rotations and, with the swing
from the last bend, his eyes followed the whizzing metal.
The throws were marked by arrows dug into the sand.
Nearly all grouped on one spot. Their feathers, increasing in number, resembled a bed of corn-ears on an empty
race-track. No one could boast of any definite superiority.

The novices, when they finally had their turn, fared
worse. They blamed the weight of their discs, which were
adjusted to the Olympic standard. They were all made
of massive bronze and were heavier than those used in
the gymnasiums and Games elsewhere. Sotion, who was
used to a stone discus bulkier and of a larger diameter,
could not manipulate this slippery little object. Gloomy
and with dishevelled hair, he opened his mouth after
every throw ready to hurrah, but again bit his lips when
the slave stuck in the arrow at a discreditable distance.
Losing command over himself and seizing the disengaged discs which were lying about on the ground,
he ran and hurled them as if he was the sole occupant
of the stadium. At last the rod of the hellanodikes recalled him to order. He flinched as the red weal came up
on his back, leapt aside and burst out into a loud hearty
laugh.

The exercises continued. Hysmon pointed out the
futility of wild swinging of the arms. He corrected the
faults in the alternate pivoting of the legs when they
changed over during the spin. He explained to them
about the centre of gravity and where it ought to be
when the trunk was bent. He pointed out to his audience
the importance of economy of effort in the movements
of the various muscles exerted during the throw. He
was vexed with the elder ones because they repeatedly

committed the same incorrigible faults. He scolded one
of the aleiptai and threatened him with the rod, should
he fail to rectify the inefficiency of his charge.

After a while he gave the order for the collection and
removal of the arrows from the race-track, bidding that
their marks be spread over with sand. A second slave
appeared with a bundle of javelins. Smilax, who from
noon onwards had been blowing his aulos without an
interval, received a goblet of wine.

The javelin was a straight shaft of the thickness of a
finger and no taller than the height of an average man.
At its centre a strap was attached, with a hanging loop,
which was to prevent slipping; for this purpose it was
bound tightly round and tied firmly to the smooth shaft.
With two fingers—the index and middle ones—inserted
into the loop, the shaft was held above the shoulder
when throwing. Each boy, on being summoned, took a
short run to the *balbis* and, flinging back his shoulders,
hurled the javelin with all the force at his command.

To avoid treading on the line proved now more difficult than with the discs, for here they ran with head
slightly turned and the eyes fixed on the javelin, the
correct poise for which was forwards from the loop at an
acute angle with the horizontal. This position assured
a long throw.

The attention of all focused on the two eternally silent
Arcadians. With javelin in hand they were suddenly
transformed into mountaineers and hunters. There was
no trouble with the line for them because they did not
use the short run to the *balbis* in their style. Standing
straight, with the arm forming a perfect right-angle at
the elbow, they directed their attention for a fleeting

second to the javelin dangling in the loop and discharged it with a sharp jab, as if they were aiming at an animal from an ambush. The left arm, which all the others swung fiercely backwards, remained with them motionless at their side. A watchful pose, passed down from generation to generation, had fettered it thus to prevent any sudden incautious movement which might stir the twigs in the brushwood. Their throws covered almost one third of the stadium.

Sodamos, who had spent with them many long months and had daily witnessed their faultless skill, uttered each time a shout of admiration:

"By Heracles! Even if you were to practise all your life you would never equal them!"

"Yes," Epharmostos admitted, "but with the javelin alone you do not attract attention at Olympia, and it seems they can do nothing else."

"One cannot be sure. Their running is not bad. In the leaps, too, they will certainly improve. And with that much one can squeeze through to the pentathlon."

Up came Eutelidas, running:

"I cannot get accustomed to the javelin used here. With us in Sparta the javelin has a sharp head and is aimed at a particular spot. On a post hangs a target with a painted eye. I was able to hit the actual eye from forty feet and further."

"By Athena," whispered Gryllos to Sotion, "it is said the Spartans never lie!"

The day, divided into five sections like an apple, still kept, between the lengthened shadows and the dusk, its sweetest morsel—wrestling. Bearing this in mind, they were able to endure the disappointment of worthless throws, unskilful leaps, and their failures with the discus and spear. Their bodies, made awkward by an irritating loss of self-confidence, were refreshed by the desire for combat. They pictured their relief when at last they should escape from these monotonously insignificant results and start anew; the pleasure in feeling again their real selves in the clutch of an adversary! For a moment which is gone without a trace you were among the hundreds of movements just like your own. You failed, you faded away more swiftly than the mist between the spearpoint and its contemptible mark. But now you will exist in all your bulk. A stranger will feel the weight of your presence and honour you with the closest attention.

As soon as they were ordered to proceed to the Tetragonon, they swarmed through the door leading out from the sacred track.

The brownish-yellow quadrangle of sand was surrounded by a low wall. This part of the gymnasium, facing west, was filled with sunshine. As soon as they got there, the elder set threw themselves down and began to roll in the sand. The rest followed their example and to the accompaniment of shouts and laughter they became a tangled mass of bodies which raised a cloud of dust. A thick layer of dust adhered to the oiled limbs. Queer figures emerged, whose nakedness was hid beneath the grime. The hellanodikes with the end of his rod pointed out places that were not yet sandy. These spots were especially on the nape and shoulders. The intention was to make the bodies easier to hold.

At last the first pair was called. Both bent sideways and, stretching out their arms, immediately seized each other in a clinch. Hysmon called out, but they did not understand. It was only the rod that separated them. Instantly the world lost its charm.

The hellanodikes wanted to know at the start how much stamina, muscular development and knowledge of the rules the newcomers possessed. He therefore did not allow the bouts proper to commence, but by turns all the holds which tradition had inherited from the gods and heroes were enacted. The traditions of the gymnasium contained accounts of the methods which Athena had taught the first men. They described the tactics which gave fame to the victories of Heracles over Antaios, of Theseus over Kerkyon and of Peleus over the silver-footed Thetis. These were subjects that were always vital. They were discussed as if the bouts had taken place only yesterday. Sculptors carved them on the metopes of temples. Potters painted them on urns and bowls. They became living words, the technical terms by which the holds were defined.

Hysmon was sparing with his directions—just two or three words each time. Pronounced as they were in the Elean dialect, they were not always understood, and on other occasions only a few knew what was implied. Most often their meaning was grasped through the last-minute inspiration prompted, so it seemed, by terror in the rear where the swung rod whistled. The opponents threw themselves on each other and again stepped back. They seized each other's arms, necks and thighs. These were, however, isolated acts: the living illustration of technical terms. The whole affair looked much more like a language lesson than like wrestling exercises.

Repeatedly they returned to the primary stance. The feet were firmly set on the ground and the flexed toes

55

dug into the sand to get a good purchase. The trunk, with the back arched, rested firmly on widely separated legs, and the neck hid itself between the shoulder-blades. The knees trembling with taut control, the straining eyes and the ever-ready outstretched arms played the silent drama of a fight which was denied them. Hysmon carefully scrutinised the muscles of their thighs and calves and the tendons at their knees. Little Glaukos reeled as soon as Timasarchos caught him by the ankle. The hellanodikes recalled him and ordered Xenophon to repeat the same hold. But the boy had evidently had enough. He calculated every movement ahead, for right from the preliminary posture he went out to the attack. Firmly grasping his opponent's forearm, he held it so that the other could not free himself. Within the next second he had turned completely round, ready to toss his adversary over his back. But Timasarchos thrust his disengaged left arm under Xenophon's armpit and both, turning over like the sails of a windmill, fell to the ground.

The hellanodikes gave the rod back to the slave and sat on the bench near the wall. The older set greeted this with cheers. Sotion, standing in the centre of the stadium, scarlet from the sun pouring down on him, with his eyes shaded by his palm, did not know what had occasioned the cheering. Eutelidas leapt at him like a wildcat and they started wrestling. From all sides challenges were issued. Each one chose an antagonist. The exercises had come to an end; now was the time for unconventional wrestling.

The Tetragonon seethed with tussling figures. Numerous pairs entwined and disentangled themselves, leapt away from each other, got mixed up with other couples and, having lost the original opponent, continued their bouts with someone else. Sometimes this was mere cunning; the antagonist had intentionally strayed. The wrestling had appeased his longing for those mute moments of admiration, pleasure and emotion. A thousand unexplained impulses of the struggle with a challenged opponent were sensed in innumerable flashes during the day of exercises.

They did not adhere to the recognised rules of the game, which ceased the moment one wrestler was brought down, but, having fallen, they would roll on the ground. There were intervals when the stadium was a mass of bodies choking with exertion. Occasionally there would ring out a sudden gay laugh like the chirping of a bird: youth had found a freedom utterance which had hitherto been restrained.

The two "guardians of the law", whose approach no one had perceived, stood at the wicket-gate. Leaning on their long staves, grey-haired and white, and absolutely still, they looked like statues in a graveyard. Not remembering the names and unable to distinguish the features of these young faces resembling overworked suns which, from time to time, peered out from the scrambling mass, they recognised in them the past Olympiads: the grand contests of every fourth year. Memory raised the animation of their thoughts higher and higher until it toppled from the dizzy peak of their own youth. Then with a deep sigh they inhaled into their lungs the pungent aroma of manly sweat, which for them had a flavour more refreshing than sea air.

Hysmon, looking up at the sky, which now had lost

its twilight, clapped his hands. The stadium rang with shouts, and from the dust of the sand emerged human shapes, as if this were the moment of the world's creation.

All gathered at the well situated at the other end of the Tetragonon in a separate courtyard. With a scraper, a flat longish blunt sickle, they removed the sand that had encrusted on their oiled skin. Pataikos drew water for them all, his whole body bent far over the parapet as he did so. Filled pails were passed round and they poured them over each other in turn. Every minute a cool shower was splashed against someone's chest or back. Many cleaned themselves with sponges, but some of them used natron, a lixiviated salt. The trainers rubbed their pupils with thick towels, while others ran about in order to get themselves dry in the air.

Gradually the well was left deserted, as the competitors departed for their evening meal. All that remained were small pools formed by the water that had been poured around. In the darkened night under the stars the shadowy forms of some women were seen moving about. They were collecting from the ground the mingled grease of dust, olive-oil and sweat. From this they prepared a salve to strengthen the bones of weakly children. After a while they also disappeared and the slaves closed the two gates—the one facing the Street of Silence and the other, beside the sepulchral monument of Achilles, leading to the Agora.

CHAPTER V

THE COSMOS

T HE gymnasium gradually filled. Day after day there emerged from the hellanodikeon scores of young men who, streaming past the stadium, disappeared into the residential chambers. There was speculation about their homes. Those who were closer asked them direct questions, and their answers spoke of ever different regions, ranged over the names of known towns along the road by which the spondophoros had come. The names of forgotten villages resounded dully, and certain sounds made chaos in the head. The compass turned round and round, with no point at which it could come to rest, and distant colonies announced themselves with the proud surge of waves beating on the shores of myth.

Everybody hastily tidied up his belongings in order to be as early as possible at the stadium. Those coming from Akarnania, Aetolia and Epeiros always forgot to divest themselves of the boots they wore on their journey and these left heavy tracks on the sand from their rows of studs. Others again found it difficult to part with their chitons, and in the end, when they did disrobe, they retained their loincloths.

It was obvious that these were of the border tribes, whose barbarian prejudice had adulterated Greek customs. The most reluctant were the Ionians from Asia

Minor, the neighbours of the Orient. The hellanodikai merely shrugged their shoulders at their bashfulness. Complete nudity was obligatory only at Olympia. At the fifteenth Olympiad, two centuries and a half ago, Orsippos lost his loincloth while racing and received his wreath naked. The result of that accident became a fixed custom.

Their companions, however, were less indulgent than the hellanodikai. Especially the Spartans and the other Dorians—who by an enduring heritage had no bashfulness—were derisive of the modest ones.

"With us even the girls are nude when competing," said Eutelidas, voicing his indignation.

They were enveloped by ribald hints that they were circumcised. They were nicknamed Persians. A few of the youths, on the verge of tears, persisted in their naive obstinacy. But as soon as they ceased to attract further attention, nobody noticed when the last loincloth was discarded.

At times the discipline of the exercises was disturbed by some fantastic newcomer. A negro slave attending a certain competitor from Kytene attracted a crowd. He was therefore prohibited from showing himself in the gymnasium, and so, during the whole period he spent his time in his master's room in song. It was not real singing, for he was afraid to raise his voice. He hummed with lips tightly closed, and in still moments the air reverberated with a resonant buzz as if some large beetle were trying to escape. A week later the Kyrenaean shifted into the town.

His name was Telesikrates. He registered for the race with arms. This seemed to be at cross purposes with nature, which had distinctly destined his compact figure and the wide breadth of his shoulders for wrestling. From his statements it was learned that his choice did not consider physical conditions, but was directed by his ancestral records. One of his forebears, Alexidamos, received the hand of a Libyan princess for racing.

"This took place in Irasa," he told them. "King Antaios organised the races and promised his daughter to the champion. The girl was the goal. She stood in the open field, two stades away from the start, in her wedding dress and with a wreath on her head. Twenty young men competed in the race, all of good parentage, friends of the King. My great-grandfather won. He outstripped everyone by a few paces, seized the girl by the arm as though she were the goal-post, and turned round with her. By Ammon!"

Sotion induced him repeatedly to relate some fresh detail which amused everybody. Sotion was peerless in his seriousness and curiosity. To every word he added his "By Zeus!" "Impossible!" "Marvellous!" slapping the Kyrenaean's back. And when the latter was exhausted, and surreptitiously rubbed his reddened shoulder-blade, Sotion said:

"Shame on you! Whoever made his great-grandmother dance?"

"Great-grandmother you say? At that time she was the most beautiful girl in all Libya."

"In Libya? Why didn't you say so at once?"

Telesikrates stood aghast to find such knavery.

"They're laughing at me," he said to his negro in the evening.

"Because, obviously, they don't know how rich your father is."

The following morning Telesikrates was the first in the stadium, and scarcely had the competitors assembled before he commenced a detailed account of how many fields, orchards, vineyards, cattle, slaves and ships old Karneades owned. His enumeration had reached the barns, when Sotion exploded:

"By Heracles! Stop or you'll smother us with corn and choke us!"

Sodamos alone listened carefully to all the information. He cogitated; it could be turned to good account later on perhaps. They drifted to some other topic, but again the Kyrenaean became their laughing-stock. He was almost ashamed now of his golden scraper. Before noon, however, he did some worthy sprinting and after the interval he devoted himself to boxing. They remembered some of his punches and before the end of the day it was clear that, without the help of a great-grandmother and without the riches of a father, one could still be of some importance in this world.

Nevertheless it was a period crowded with incident. The previous day vanished without a trace with the arrival of a flock of newcomers. Such a man as Gerenos, for instance, could dim with his shadow a dozen such men as Telesikrates.

The first sign of Gerenos was his trail on the sand. He had found his way in one day before dawn. Squeezing himself through a side wicket-gate, the latch of which must have forced open perhaps by an absent-minded push of his, he wandered all over the sports enclosure before he hit upon the hellanodikeon. Some time later

Sotion, ambling out of his lodgings, espied titanic foot-marks deeply imprinted on the ground. It was a grey misty morning. There was calm under an overcast sky. The gymnasium was without a sound. The Tarentine wheeled round a number of times: not a soul was to be seen. He was seized with fear. A childish terror gripped his throat and paralysed his legs. These footprints—which belonged to none of the competitors, which, as it seemed to him, could belong to no human—conjured up a formidable presence. "Heracles!" He could not banish the thought and even closed his eyes and shrieked aloud at his mad conjecture.

"You should have seen me. You should have seen me," he related choking with laughter, "how I stood there. My limbs were leaden or of clay and I peered at those tracks as over an abyss. I tell you, as over an abyss, for in my imagination they grew so immense that I would have sworn only two of them covered the whole stadium."

He was rescued, subsequently, by Sodamos, whose mercantile assessing eye immediately recognised that the tread was merely a trifle larger than the standardised foot measure.

"And at our place," said Philon, from Jyras at the mouth of the Boh, "they show a footprint of Herkules a cubit long."

Sodamos lifted his head with a shake of denial:

"That is a fairy-tale. Heracles was of normal build. All that is said about him in every corner of the world should not be credited. In Olympia, and not in any Jyras, he stamped his actual foot on the stadium, and everyone can satisfy himself that it is only a trifle larger than mine or yours."

"But none of us would achieve even one of his feats," came from Philon, shrugging his shoulders.

"Because none of us is the son of a god, behind none of us stands Athena, and none of us possesses his great soul. Heracles was strong, surpassing all strength imaginable. Milon of Croton was a child before him. But strength alone did not comprise his mightiness. His was a soul without fear. He was conscious that he could dare anything. He felt certain of fulfilling any exploit. He was patient and persevering. He could journey to the world's end with not a thought of where he would sleep nor of what he would eat. Who is able to endure so many days of solitude as he did, and that in the mountains, too, in deserts, in wild regions where everyone was his enemy? He regarded no danger, neither the strength of the lion nor of the giant with whom he strove. He thought only of the combat itself, that it must be contested and that he had to be the victor."

Sodamos had never yet spoken in such a mood. Under the swarthy growth his cheeks suffused with blushes. It seemed an internal fire—the flaming and passionate soul with which he had never been credited—had suddenly peeped out from its impregnable retreat. His comrades had an obscure feeling of uneasiness. No one knew what the reason was for this outburst: had a divine spark of unexpected ecstasy momentarily kindled within him and illumined for him incidents around which human conjectures blundered? Had a woeful sincerity brought to light some buried experience, some strife between desires and inability? Unwillingly they turned their gaze away from him to allow him to cool down. It was not till some time had elapsed that Gryllos began:

"But this footprint is larger than the one in Olympia."

His words fell on empty silence. They had just begun on the olive-oil when suddenly there entered the person who had engrossed their minds since dawn.

Nobody was disillusioned. He was taller by a head than Eurymenes of Samos, the tallest of the competitors. Everybody appeared minute beside his thighs, chest and the width of his shoulders. Covered with black hair, with a thick black beard and bushy eyebrows, he rather resembled a savage. By his short crop, however, one recognised the wrestler. The first to accost him was Gryllos:

"By Zeus! It would have been better to have burnt that hair off your body."

Gerenos, who was engaged with his kynodesmos, stopped at the shoulder-strap and eyed Gryllos with such an expression that one did not know whether he was astonished or annoyed. After a time, from within the beard, there came some discordant sounds which became intelligible only after a while:

"That does not come under the rules."

"To be comely certainly comes under rules older than Olympia, shaggy one!"

In vain the giant searched for someone's help. Even the boys were emboldened by his helpless silence. Glaukos, spying two white hairs on his temples, exclaimed:

"Why did you come so late, poor grandfather?"

But Gryllos insinuated:

"In the year of Marathon he was already on the move, but he had a long road and was delayed."

As a matter of fact he came from Naukratis at the mouth of the Nile. In the midst of this jesting he stood with bowed head and deeply furrowed forehead, as if he felt there was something improper in the great distance. Eventually Sotion drew him aside, good Sotion, though even he addressed him as "ancestor".

No one remembered such a gathering as this. All the gymnasiums, it seemed, had opened like a sluice discharging a swollen stream of youth into Elis. The lodgings lacked space and houses in the town were hired at wildly exorbitant rents. Many slept the nights under canvas. The hellanodikai doubled the rigidity of the regulations. Only the hardiest sinews and the most masterly skill could survive in the stadium. Those who were eliminated had not the courage to return home. They loitered about, swinging *halteres* in some remote corner near the wall, lifting discs, measuring the javelin-throws, helping others to strew sand over themselves or assisting in washing it off in the evening. They were happy if someone called out their name, as the hellanodikai did not. Usually it was not for long that they enjoyed this life in the background, because the increasing congestion soon pushed them beyond the walls.

.   .   .   .

The entire gymnasium is now astir.

Coming from the river through the Street of Silence and passing the temple of Artemis Philomeirax—the goddess who loves striplings—is a file of competitors. On their heads they are carrying hydrias of water. From the courtyard of the gymnasium they turn right and enter a spacious rectangle surrounded by a wall. Their comrades are already at work. Scattered here and there, they are breaking up the earth with picks, gathering

stones and throwing them into a corner of the training
enclosure. The ground, dug up all over and levelled, is
watered until it becomes a quagmire in which the legs
sink to above the ankles. It reduces the force of a fall,
but it conceals the danger spots for slithering feet, and
bodies become slippery from rolling in it.

This is the Maltho or "Soft Field", the area for the
pancration.

The pancration combines wrestling and boxing. All
grasps and blows are permissible. There is almost no part
of the body immune from punches and kicks. Crushing
and twisting the fingers and toes, covered by age-old
usage, are accepted terms in its technical phraseology.

It is indeed a virile contest, a combat for primed bodies
and souls. No one who has doubts about his maturity,
his physique, or his preparation, would dare to come to
the Soft Field. Aipytos, supervising the training, hardly
ever raises his voice. If he interrupts a bout at all, it is
chiefly to counsel or indicate a method of defence to one
in a hopeless situation who had not seen it.

But to-day he expelled two contestants from the gymnasium: one an Eleian and the other, it seems, from
Argos. Apparently there was nothing about which they
could be reproached. Everybody is at liberty to form his
own opinion about the incident. For aught one knows,
he may have detected in them some expression of ill-
temper? Tightened lips or suffused eyes after an unexpected blow? But you may depend on Aipytos: he
rescues you from a dangerous opponent, one of the sort
that is capable of kicking at the tenderest part, of ram-
ming fingers down a throat or into the nostrils, of gouging
out eyes. Would not a flogging have been given in

Olympia? A slight retribution for the marring of such a great festival.

Beyond the wall of the Soft Field the boxers are creating a hubbub. Their bodies, sturdy, thickset and powerful, have muscles which show a bold contour. Their massive skulls make them appear like men of another race.

They were putting on the straps. These were narrow thin strips of cowhide, only steeped in grease and not tanned. Each measured ten feet in length. First a loop was made at one end, and into this the hand was inserted, leaving the thumb free. The strap was then wound round each finger in turn and then round all four fingers held together. This binding was done in such a manner that the fingers could be bent at their joints and the fist clenched. The strap was finally passed over the back of the hand and a number of turns made at the wrist and some way up the forearm, finishing up by tucking the end under the firmly wrapped coils.

There—the left hand is ready. The right hand is more difficult to fix up. "Hold my strap"—"Zeus, it has slipped out again"—"Grasp it with your teeth"—"Just bind my little finger." The boys, with the help of their aleiptai, have had their straps adjusted properly. Some, here and there, donned a protecting skull-cap also. This was lined with cloth and had ear-guards attached, which dulled the hearing. Agesidamos, as impatient as a spark, darted off to the corner of the arena, where from a bough hung the korykos.

This was a bag made of pigskins sewn together. It was filled with sand and had retained the shape of an animal with paws rigidly outstretched. Agesidamos vented his spleen on it, testing the precision of his eye and the power of his punches; while the bag took his blows with dull thuds, rocking freely and dejectedly in its lifeless impotence.

   .   .   .   .

The Tetragonon resounded with laughter. Gerenos rolled in the sand, and now stood up unlike any earthly creature. Here came Kapros, the president of the hellanodikai. The laughter subsided, to break out again as soon as he left.

His name meant "wild boar", but something else besides. A hundred times a day the same unpleasant jokes were repeated about him. These broke the monotony of the respect this strange stately personage commanded.

Every day, two or three times, he walked all over the training grounds, stopping nowhere. On his way he glanced about, it would seem, cursorily and absentmindedly. But he recognised everybody, he noticed everything. And when the next morning Hysmon or Aipytos or someone else called you up and ran his hands over your thigh, you might be sure it was Kapros who had directed his attention to your misshapen muscle, the result of bad training. Such eyes saw, one would say, further than the present, and one judged intuitively that he knew already the names which the herald would announce on the Olympic stadium on the day of the sacred full moon.

   .   .   .   .

A new batch hurries out from the hellanodikeon. Passing the tomb of Achilles, each one lifts his thumb to his lips as a mark of respect. In the small enclosure they started to undress, and began rubbing themselves with olive-oil. They had queer haughty airs. Gryllos struck up an acquaintance with them. They answered off-handedly and adopted slow and leisurely movements as if they wished to appear important. He ascertained eventually that among them were a few champions of the Isthmian Games, which had just finished.

"They might be a bit more modest," thought Gryllos, but their words certainly made an impression on him. From their accounts one gathered an idea of an avenue of tall and slender pines, the temple of Poseidon, the sacred circle and the stadium lying in an ancient river-bed. On both sides of the Isthmus of Corinth the blue sea stretches out: two routes of the great world by which people have come in ships to this human ant-hill.

"It's full as never before," said one, and Gryllos admitted to himself that it is difficult to disregard a man whom the applause of an immense crowd had exalted above the rest.

"And do any of you compete in the hoplite-race?" he inquired.

"Presently, presently, my beautiful."

Under his very nose they suddenly opened a casket. In it lay a wreath of dry celery leaves, an Isthmian wreath entwined with red ribbon. Its significance was beyond all words, and heads at once bent over the casket, even Gerenos peering down from his height. But Sotion, popping up suddenly from somewhere, in the very centre, tipped the stranger under the chin and riveted his mirthful eyes upon him.

"Only don't forget," he says, "that the olive grows taller than celery."

Of course, throughout the day nothing else was talked

about. Hysmon, meanwhile, was starting the first exercise with the novices. Everybody was curious for news from the sacred track.

"Nothing extraordinary."

"One is a good runner. His name is Dandis."

"From where?"

"They say from Argos."

"I said so. Only the rabble gravitate to the Isthmus."

"You saw how Hysmon made a wry face when told where they come from."

"That was because of something else. Here they do not talk about the Isthmus."

"Why?"

"That comes from as far back as the time of Heracles. The Eleians are bound by an oath, hence no Eleian ever goes to the Isthmian Games."

"What is the oath?"

"I don't know exactly. It is a story older than the moon. Ask someone born here."

.   .   .   .

In the boxing arena handsome Alkimidas was being soundly beaten. His fair locks hung limp on his forehead and he reddened with humiliation. He was ashamed not because he was being thrashed but because of what the hellanodikes said:

"You smack with the open palm, just like a girl."

.   .   .   .

Sotion came running through the Tetragonon, and paused to watch Gerenos pitted against Eurymenes.

The giant was more menacing when at rest than when wrestling. It appeared that he used his hands—those mighty hands whose every grasp seemed sure to throttle

71

—for some tame amusement. He was afraid of his
strength and stooped beneath it as under a load. The
hellanodikcs reprimanded him incessantly. He became
more and more awkward. He tottered on his legs, but
just then he caught sight of Sotion—Eurymenes was in
the air and fell to the ground some paces away.

. . . .

At the well in the courtyard Menalkes removed his
cap, from under which blood was oozing. His ear had
been damaged. He drew water, bathed the part and
looked around: "I wish someone would give me a pad of
lint and some warm olive-oil. . . ."

On the sacred track Hysmon was finishing the practices
with the Isthmians. It was apparent from their disillusioned countenances that the Olympic olive really did
grow taller. Sotion peeped in from somewhere through
the wicket-gate and called: "The stadium is vacant." He
returned accompanied by a few others and they started
their private training.

They crawled on all fours, they hopped up and down,
raising their knees as high as their hips. Lying on their
backs with legs in the air, they waved them about in all
directions. They wielded their *halteres* using an overarm
swing as for the javelin. They tossed the discs into the
air, and caught them again. Eutelidas jumped upwards
tapping his rump with his heels at every hop and counting: "601, 602, 603." Seeing that Pataikos was gazing at
him in astonishment, he said without interrupting his
jumps:

"At home—this is called—bibasis—605—and the girls
—go—606—up to a thousand taps."

Agesidamos of Lokri had won a good boxing bout and

now he was sprawling on the turf, while his aleiptes Ilas, sprinkling water on him, massaged his nape and thighs. Suddenly the youth brushed his hands aside and ran after Sotion. They chased each other on the sacred track. Sotion slackened his pace and came to a halt. As the other one reached him, he laid his palms on the boy's shoulders and leaped over him with a single vault. Now he had reached the group of discus-throwers. After a moment, when called for his turn to throw, he stepped out serenely as if he had not moved from the line.

It was some time now since he had got used to the lump of bronze. Again his line lay half a foot beyond that of Sodamos.

"You are advancing to the wreath over my back," his friend whispered to him with not a shadow of envy.

They loved each other because they were worthy of each other. It could not be termed friendship if one considered the other slightly inferior. Both were aware of their merits. Sodamos was stronger and maturer. He knew exactly how much he could expect from his sinews. Sotion was developing steadily. Every day a fresh petal blossomed out from that human flower. There was no saying beforehand what he could not do. Seemingly his performances were the result not of effort but of inspiration.

Sodamos put his arms round him and his palm rested on his friend's heart. Sotion returned the embrace unthinkingly:

"Look at Ischomachos," he said. "Who would have expected it? You remember when he first came how he did the turn, how he trampled the line? I did not see him running to-day."

73

"He was very good," answered Sodamos, observing too what Sotion did not notice, that after every throw Ischomachos looked backwards with a searching glance for Sotion.

Pataikos came running from the Soft Field:

"Kallias is wrestling now. Come, it is worth watching."

"The Athenian?" inquired Sotion. "No, I cannot; I have still a couple of throws with the discus."

. . . .

"Mind the strap, it is not bound tight enough. It's slipping down the shaft."

"I did three stades to-day."

"This is the second time I have had to oil myself."

"How is Telesikrates getting on?"

"If he had followed the promptings of the gods, who meant him for a boxer, he would certainly have achieved something. In the hoplite-race he is only good enough to decorate the tail end of a quartet."

"Pour some more water in here."

"He told him that he has too weak a neck for wrestling."

"Still, you took a mighty swing! I thought you were hurling it right into the sea and would have to pay for a new discus."

. . . .

Ergoteles, all by himself, was practising the long-distance run. Hysmon watched him and shouted:

"The heels a hair's breadth higher." And later: "What stade?"—to which Ergoteles replied in full flight:

"The eleventh."

. . . .

The hellanodikes interrupted the bout of Kallias with

Aristokleides, which had lasted too long. It was so splendid, so swift, one would like to say so passionate, if the expression could be applied to two master performers. They separated with a smile, each gave himself up to the attentions of his aleiptes, who wiped off the fatigue. Neither of them was hurt. From all the shattering assaults they had emerged with only a few insignificant bruises.

That is the real pancration. Man engages with man in complete nakedness, protected by nothing and having no weapon other than the strength of his muscles and the response of his bones and joints. It proves that the defence is adapted fittingly to the blows, which can be parried by the arm or leg.

.   .   .   .

Kapros entered the sacred track. A foursome had just finished the short run. Trails remained behind on the freshly disturbed sand. The hellanodikes ran his eyes over these and went off.

"What has he noticed there?"

Some runners are walking along the edge of the track as if searching for rare shells after the tide has gone out.

"Look, their three strides equal only two of his!"

"By Zeus!"

"Who raced here on the extreme right?"

"Skamandros of Mitylene."

.   .   .   .

Epharmostos, who is a wrestler only, does not struggle with Sotion, the pentathlon aspirant. He only plays with him. He allows him everything: "You may turn your somersaults," he says. Sotion is irritated. He collects himself and when the other one heeds him too lightly, he

75

tumbles him to the earth. The Opuntian, however, drags
Sotion after him. Catching him with one arm like a
serpent, he crushes him into the sand. "I could keep you
like that during the whole Iliad," he laughs, "and then
you would not get up any more than Hector gets up from
his pyre."

And Sotion remains stretched out, though Epharmostos has already let go. He feels the sand cutting him
between the shoulder-blades and filling the furrow made
by his spine. The biting sensation of defeat spreads over
his whole body. Epharmostos's words, which he has
already forgotten, have cast over him a gloom as of some
great and sad event. He slides his tongue over his parched
lips, which taste bitter. "So tastes defeat." He shrouds
himself with the stadium as if it were a chlaina and hides
under it like a child that is afraid of ghosts in the night.
His eyes open. Over him is the vast heaven with the
amber streaks of the setting sun. When he arises, a shiver
runs through him as if with his feet he had trodden on
his own grave. He bounds into the air and dashes off:
Alalà!

.   .   .   .

During the spell of a short summer night it was only
sleep that stilled this flurry of movement. The break of
dawn, through a chink in the wall, narrow as an em-
brasure in a battlement, invaded his room and startled
him. It seemed that a wire-spring had suddenly flicked
him. Sotion sprang out of bed and with a few strides
leapt down the stairs. He called, shouting at the top
of his voice and in a moment the whole building was
immersed in the glow of his dawn. Throughout the rest
of the day he was the living example of Herakleitos's

idea: that fire animated the human being. It seemed that even the air quivered around him, as if actually he remained in a glowing state. Bodies and souls were affected by him. The hellanodikai could not call to mind such a bustle, such an eagerness as now prevailed over the sports arena. People who in the first days were of no account matured like saplings transplanted under a hotter sky.

In its uninterrupted activity the gymnasium resembled a whirling solar system. In the centre was the nucleus, a group of the hardiest competitors, forming an orbit for Sotion. To belong to it, to breathe the air of the most heated combat, to live in the sincere truth of one's own doughty deeds, became the ambition of each one the moment he had settled his belongings in the lodging-house and had got accustomed to the practice ground. But a month could have gone by without the day coming when one of these demigods would step forward with a generous word and raise the value of your effort, to put his arm around you like a purple scarf. At the circumference of this distinguished circle there hovered many such as Telesikrates, who were always kept at a jocular distance.

A little further on, a separate circle with its own arrangement of stars and planets comprised the best athletes among the boys. It was a sphere particularly charming in its inaccessible modesty, teeming with satellites—the old and vigilant trainers. From the various groups of runners, boxers, pancratiasts, wrestlers, there emerged small constellations of a dubious lustre. At times comets ascended. These drew nearer to the central nucleus, but after some days disappeared in an unknown direction.

At the remotest part of the horizon, resembling a belt of the Milky Way, there swarmed a crowd scarcely to be told apart. It was a pulp-like mass of bodies whose names no one knew.

CHAPTER VI

IKKOS OF TARENTUM

O<small>N</small> a certain day, from this mass a new competitor emerged. Sotion was told about him:

"There is someone from your district, from Tarentum."

The ephebe gazed at him and for a moment across his mind's eye there fleeted portions of streets, a truncated wall visible above a garden, the palestra planted round with fig-trees, a small creek with a boat moored at the beach, until finally, as if recognising a face in the crowd, he called out:

"Ikkos!"

The latter turned round and gave him his hand:

"How you have grown!" he remarked.

"We parted company while still at school. But you were older than I."

Ikkos's cheeks were covered by a dusky down. Except for this their bodies seemed to be of the same maturity. Sotion's lips trembled, but the words which caused this trembling were left unuttered. Ikkos continued:

"Yes, I have shifted over to Croton. It was after my father's death. For the past year my mother has been with me. I work in Tisikrates's gymnasium. The old man took me in as his assistant and one makes a living somehow or other. Even now he provided for my journey."

"But you were registered——"

"——as a Tarentine, of course. At any rate there I have my house, my fields and guardians. By Heracles! I must return and settle with them."

Sotion puckered his eyelids, unable to bear the dark spiteful look which dilated the nut-brown eyes of Ikkos.

"What are you going in for?" asked he hurriedly.

"Pentathlon."

"Then we will be together again." And, taking his leave with a smile, he ran off in answer to someone's beckoning call.

Ikkos's activities, however, did not begin till noon. At the common meal he ate a fish. It was really an actual fish and furthermore the most common sort of fish that could be had, but even if the stadium had changed into a lake with tritons and nereids, astonishment could not have been greater.

"Where did you get the fish?"

"If you mean to say that he caught it and scaled and boiled it, then I am not going to believe you," said Gryllos. "Where? The boy who acts as his aleiptes brought it for him."

"Did you see him?" questioned Pataikos.

"No, Boeotian, I do not need to see in order to find out such a common thing."

Common thing? Gryllos calls it a "common thing" that a competitor, on the very day of arrival and after a full morning of exercises, has had the time to send his servant into town and treat himself to something special for dinner! Nobody has been able to do that for many months. What a number of questions poured forth all at once! When did he think of it? Not knowing the town, where did he send his servant? Where did he find out what kind of meal they would give him in the gymnasium? And finally, why could he not wait till to-morrow, for what reason did he need the fish so urgently?

They kept silent thereafter. They tried even not to look in Ikkos's direction, but when eventually one or two glances did stray again towards the Tarentine, he was at that very moment handing back to his servitor the thoroughly chewed backbone of the fish for him to throw away somewhere. All eyes watched the attendant in the hope that a chance would come to shout at him, should he deposit it in some inappropriate place. But he left the gymnasium and everybody supposed that he had found the rubbish-pit without mistake. This added to their annoyance. The full measure of such common-sense and tidiness was in itself somewhat offensive. Everybody was piqued by the memory of his own timidity and clumsiness during the first days.

At a dragging pace the donkey came along with the jar of water. The earthen bowl began to circulate. The cold draughts were gulped down with a deep sigh and the empty vessel was returned each time with the same unsatisfied avidity. Ikkos in his turn, having received the goblet, did not move but remained lying just as he was and placed the vessel beside himself on the sand. The competitors looked at each other: does he imagine he is lounging at a banquet? With almost a yell Kallias, who was to drink after him, demanded:

"Quicker, others are waiting too!"

Ikkos, seemingly astonished, replied:

81

"Let it warm a bit, it is too cold."

This was beyond belief. The fish, though it still required explanation, belonged, at least, to the sphere of human volition in which everybody was free to make his own choice. But to start an argument about water, to accept suspiciously the priceless gift of the gods which on this torrid earth is never abundant—that indeed is real heresy. Several of them could not refrain from telling him so. Their words were harsh but their full import was lost in noisy vituperation, such was the fury which overcame them.

Ikkos was truly taken by surprise. He sat up and took the bowl in his hand:

"For Hermes!" said he and poured almost the whole of its contents on the earth. There remained but one mouthful. This he drank, but it was seen that before swallowing he kept the water for a while in his mouth.

After him Kallias followed, without once severing the contact between his lips and the vessel.

"Your stomach will catch a chill sometime," warned Ikkos.

For the first time he raised a laugh from them.

"But we were wrong, lads," announced Gryllos, "we took him for an athlete and he is a doctor."

"Can you give me something for a toothache?"

"Maybe you have some miraculous salve for the feet, to make them run faster?"

Those who were most roused immediately racked their brains for the worst and most spiteful nicknames—"Butcher!" "Tanner!" They bade him sell vegetables in the market. Finally someone with one word—cobbler—dumped him at the very bottom of the human scale.

Cobbler—that is, a man with a pale face and a warped spine, a man in a dingy hovel shunned by the air. A cobbler is a man who is always crouched down, and his miserable shape is the most horrid spectre of a sordid and stagnant existence.

None of them really despised work, many of them had come from it and would return to it, but in this sanctum of body-culture they felt themselves to be a community raised above the level of the world of ordinary beings who are weary, who toil and suffer; people who count money, sell and buy; people who live in houses, sleep under a warm chlaina and lengthen the day by the miserable glimmer of a lamp. And as if enveloped by the nauseating smell of the monotonous vulgar life, they suddenly stopped their hubbub. But a few voices were still audible.

"Give him over to us for Sparta," growled Eutelidas; "they would dust his skin there."

"Sotion, what queer fellow is this who comes from Tarentum?"

Sotion, however, shrugged his shoulders, so they left Ikkos, who remained lying on the turf with eyes half closed, as if he did not hear what was going on over his head. The afternoon exercises dispersed them in different directions. For all that, the curious individual gave them no peace. Again and again someone peeped over at the sacred track and returned with news that contained no reference to any "tanner" or "butcher". Ikkos acquitted himself well. Hysmon's rod was given no opportunity to satisfy their hostile desires. The only consolation for them was his rebuke to the servant who ran up to measure his master's jump. Hysmon shouted:

"That is no concern of yours."

It was not much, yet it gave them a certain relief. The gymnasium felt that it had returned within the bounds of recognised authority and custom.

But at the discus, Ikkos suddenly remarked to Sotion: "The sun is too strong for exercises."

"Then carry a parasol with you."

Sotion's repartee was so pleasing that they thrilled with joy as they repeated it. Skamandros from Mitylene actually began singing it. He ceased abruptly and smacked his forehead, for suddenly he had remembered a lampoon—a lampoon of old Anakreon of Teos! In it mention was made of a certain Artemon, an effeminate man, a dandy. The verses were sent down, apparently, as a smile from the gods:

> Kyke's little boy carries
> An ivory-handled parasol. . . .

It was taken up by a whole chorus. And later, indeed, by everyone separately "Son of Kyke—Ikkos." "Pais Kykes—Ikkos." "Skiadiske! Skiadeion! Skiadeion!" The word parasol, in the tones of all the dialects, was repeated beyond the limits of human tolerance. Skiadeion! This word reduced the youths to childish mockery. Little Glaukos got so obsessed by it that in spite of scoldings and beatings, in spite of a thousand painful tosses, he was no longer able to govern his fifteen-year-old spirits and continued thus until dusk. There was an impression that even Gerenos was near to laughter.

The following day many were surprised at the sight of Ikkos on the training ground. Apparently for many of them he had vanished completely once they had slept.

It seemed most likely that they would see him slinking from the enclosure of the Soft Field, that was the way he would go, laden with his things, through the courtyard, through the hellanodikai's premises, having for all company his shadow on the large empty square. At any rate no one was prepared for the calmness on his face and the keen look from beneath his heavy black eyebrows, and when he was seen engrossed in several deliberate operations—pouring out the olive-oil and rubbing it on his body, placing his back towards his attendant, who served him diligently and with never a word—the pair of them thus occupied in complete silence took on the aspect of spectral beings. They felt inclined to shout and scare away these obstinate phantoms.

However, no one spoke. There were even moments so silent that the grasshopper, primed with dew, was heard chirping frenziedly. If someone's palm tapped another's back, they were startled as if by a thunderclap. Many of the youths fretted with impatience. It was suffocating in this numbing silence. At any moment it might snap like an overbent bow. But Ikkos, having folded his kynodesme—he did this at the very end of the rubbing, not before—pointed out to his servitor the vessels scattered about on the ground, and left for the stadium.

Now one could converse at ease, but there seemed to be nothing to talk about. Occasional arguments arose about an aryballos or about a strap, but these stopped short as if the point of the quarrel had immediately been forgotten. One of the boys recalled the parasol. A few contemptuous glances were cast at him. "Stupid as a gull!" yelled Gryllos in his direction. All yesterday's laughter oppressed them like the fumes of a debauch.

Sotion alone moved about in a more rarified atmosphere. Of course, he too was altogether different. From the dawn he did not share his fund of merriment with anybody. He hid it within himself, but it was visible, nevertheless, through his beautiful smooth creamy skin. It was felt that the former harmony held sway there, that not even one string had been disturbed in this human harp. Why then did he not raise them up with just a word or a small gesture to his own state of poise?

He slipped away from their constraint because of the irrepressibility of his sparkling spirit. He was more active than ever before. Infuriated by what they would like to call his treachery, it occurred to no one to consider what could be the problems that he strove to shake off by the innumerable nimble and decisive actions, and what could be at the bottom of his engrossed attention.

He was ready next after Ikkos. He stoppered his aryballos, wiped off with his fingers the few drops of oil that remained on the rim and put the vessel beside the wall in its usual place. Without turning round, he ran off to the sacred track.

Sodamos found him there a little while later standing a few paces from the wicket-gate with his arms folded.

In the middle of the stadium Ikkos was running with knees up and short paces. He then changed his style, moving slowly with long strides, and ultimately paused on one spot marking time on his toes. The two friends watched all his movements: bends, dips, body twists and hops. In these there was nothing new. For centuries they had formed part of the exercises in the palestras and gymnasiums. But it was at once obvious that they were being done according to a definite plan; they would have liked to know the why and wherefore of the order in which these movements succeeded each other.

Sodamos remarked:

"Are we not concerning ourselves too much with him?"

"Assuredly we are."

This colloquy was heard by others, who had joined them in the meantime. The soberness of it was most soothing.

What nonsense, indeed, to pay so much attention to a man about whom so far nothing more was known than that he habitually ate fish and that he did not like cold water. Had anybody ever seen the best competitors—to whom a whole crowd of people, new and unknown, were as transparent air—begin suddenly to dwell on surmises, suspicions and whispers about an individual who to-morrow might vanish from their ken? It was too ludicrous for words, and a number of them actually burst out laughing as they ran off to their exercises.

A wave of reason and balance spread over the whole gymnasium. But it did not penetrate, of course, to the two Arcadians, unshaken as usual in their complete in-difference.

At the noon meal only a few youths peered in Ikkos's direction to see if his servant had again brought something from town. Nobody was shocked at this, for by now it was well known that Telesikrates and a few others who did not spend their nights in the gymnasium chambers arranged their breakfast just as it suited them. Even when the water came round the Tarentine was left to the very end so that he might warm his goblet to his heart's content. They had a fit of magnanimity, making way, as it were, for this frail and infirm being.

. . . .

Ikkos was not one of those persons who cease to exist once you turn your back on them. With his servitor for company, he led a life by no means lonely, though it was one of aloofness. It looked as if even on a desert island he would be full of activity. For such was his nature.

In addition to the general exercises he pursued his own course of training, an elaborate routine divided into spells of action and rest. His servant kept eyes and ears on the alert for every sign from him. All the time he was on the run for something. He fetched and carried vessels containing oil, scrapers, sponges, towels and even combs for the hair. It was not surprising to hear how he grumbled about the miserly measure of olive-oil.

"Three kyathoi for ten days—especially at this season of the year! It is insufficient even for a seven-year-old boy."

He oiled himself after nearly every event of the pentathlon. If he had any time to spare between them, he immediately lay down, and his attendant fell to massaging him, so strenuously that even the boxers' demands were trifling by comparison. Besides, he never ceased making wry faces, cursing the sun for searing the grass and thereby depriving his body of comfort on the parched ground.

He was most attentive to details when at the well in the evening. He purchased a pail for himself so that he would not be at the mercy of the general disorder. What pains he took with the scraper, first a sharper one and then one with a completely blunt edge! What a number of pailfuls of water he used! How carefully he wiped himself, first with the sponge, and then with the towel! Finally (and this was the most annoying of all) he would wrap himself in an ample woollen chlaina and vanish into the darkness like a ghost.

This bathing took up a lot of his time. He displayed a rare cunning in the way he planned his routine to finish before nightfall and thus be the first at the well. Of course, whenever a chance offered, everything was done to thwart him in this. It was a pleasure to realise that Ikkos would again lose a part of the night which was too short for him.

The night too short! Hey, Ikkos! Probably in your former existence you were a rooster and you still think you are commanding the sun!

Some of them thought it was worth while listening to him, even if it was only for a quiet giggle behind his back.

Such a thing, for instance, as the common sand: Ikkos would take up a handful, sift it through his fingers, blow on it until not even a pinch of the finer grains were left on his palm. What remained was either rough or smooth, either hard or soft, either yellow or black. Both kinds are good, they make the body supple. But he preferred the yellow sort because it makes the skin shine. There are other varieties also—mixed with clay—which are good for cleaning. But the sort which looks like brick dust induces perspiration from an over-dry body. The most appropriate sand for the cold season of the year would be that kind which is mingled with bituminous particles, because it gives warmth to the skin. Ikkos knew a great deal more. He knew, for instance, in which quarter of the world a particular thing is to be found. He enumerated countries, towns, islands and how he would establish a sand trade along the whole Mediterranean.

The trainers, for all their ripe experience, had never heard of this in their lives. Old Melesias became a child in his own estimation. He watched Ikkos so intently that it seemed he was expecting this young unlined face quickly to be creased with wrinkles and grow a long grey beard. Others, on the contrary, thought him a fine story-teller.

Ikkos paid no attention to the others' behaviour. Indifference did not worry nor ridicule affect him. If someone happened to be beside him, he opened a conversation, not caring how the other would take his words. For the most part he was unacquainted with the names of his competitors; only their bodies existed for him and, as he hailed no one, names to him were of secondary importance. From the first meeting he memorised all the details which composed the individual's physique. He kept in his mind an astonishing collection of calves, thighs, hips, chests, necks, shoulders and muscles. Whereas anybody else would say: "In Metapontum I once knew a man who——" he would say: "In Metapontum I once met a knee with such muscles that——"

Many felt flattered to belong to this assortment of human shapes. Those who appreciated this the most were the unrenowned, the common herd with vague ambitions and mediocre abilities. They were popularly known as doorkeepers, because their brief existence, between their entrance for the first time and their departure to return no more, elapsed somewhere in the vicinity of the gate. Under the yoke of the hellanodikai, disappointed in their hopes and, what was still more humiliating, condemned exclusively to the company of folk on the same level as themselves, they accepted the companionship of Ikkos as an unexpected favour of the gods.

To them he had the greatness of a champion thrice magnified. The poor runner, victim of an adverse fate, more familiar with the rod than with the goal, or the gloomy wrestler with knees lacerated by continual falls, thrilled with delight when Ikkos analysed his shortcomings. This gave them fresh courage, though they had little hope of improvement. Amongst them he found hero-worshippers. They followed him about, imitated his actions, hung upon his precepts, accepted his whole régime, treating his habits as magic rites calculated to assure them of success.

In the end he was lost to sight. Sotion's circles no longer discriminated between him and the crowd in which he had voluntarily enlisted. He found himself in the dismal background of all matters connected with the gymnasium. No one now knew when he ate or when he drank water, because he received his portion together with those who were always at the tail-end. Even the hellanodikai herded him with the weaklings.

CHAPTER VII

THE THROW OF PHAYLLOS

THE days become shorter once the summer solstice is passed. Unnoticed, the rosy dawn sheds its petals one by one. Evening beams begin to irradiate a yellow lustre. The human eye is unable to discern these changes. No clock, no appliance is able to record the evanescent fractions of time. The youthful world of the fifth century did not heed the minutes and seconds, their calculations missed out whole days as they stole by. The lunar months, clashing with the sun's even course, induced an irregularity every eight years and then three extra months were thrown in. The Greek year was sculptured with a bold chisel and nobody cared for the discarded fragments which the perpetual breezes bore away.

The gymnasium, however, recorded time like a chronometer. The most subtle sense, the instinct, had noted a few days before that the heavenly fire had passed its zenith and now everybody observed on the stadium a gliding shadow which yesterday was not yet there. The time of waiting grew shorter. The magnetic current of excitement awoke a tremor in their souls, whose pole lay in the approaching Olympic full moon. The competitors issuing forth on to the sports arena lifted their heads and looked through half-shut eyelids at the

new brightness which had emerged from behind the
Arcadian heights. They kissed their palms as a mark of
respect for the Sungod.

The temperature was high from the morning onwards. All day the gymnasium foamed and effervesced.
It was, in fact, already boiling over the brim. Competitors were pouring in once more. The hellanodikai
worked hard, straining and sweating. Hysmon, in his
sleeveless short chiton, enforced the rigid rules with his
rod. Like Odysseus at the gateway of the nether world
repelling with his sword the host of shadows pressing
forward for fresh blood, he grappled with the growing
throng, and step by step cut a path through it for the
best.

He would have liked very much to dispatch to some
other place the keen and faultless ones who had no further need of his coaching. They were allowed to do
whatever they chose. They bathed in the river, sat or
stood about chatting; on returning to the practices they
did not hear their names; seldom a hellanodikes glanced
their way, as they ran, jumped or wrestled. Surrounded
by peace, they felt as if they had escaped from a cyclone
into a smooth and calm belt.

Eventually the Pletrion was opened for them. On the
various sports fields the hellanodikai were calling out:
Ergoteles!—Dandis!—Gerenos! Epharmostos!—Sotion!
Sodamos!—Kallias! These names, foremost in the stadium, the pentathlon, boxing, wrestling and pancration,
resounded above the stilled bustle of the gymnasium, and
when the call faded away many earnestly listened to the
stillness as if there was still some hope of extracting their
own name from it. From the gymnasium, as from a ripe

pomegranate, all the juice was pressed. There remained only the peel with shreds of the pulp, from which, perhaps, a few drops could still be extracted.

The Pletrion was called the "Vestibule of Olympia". It was opened only for those who were sure to stand before the altar of Zeus. The selected band left the training grounds, a number taking their equipment with them. It seemed that with their departure everything would come to an end and that the gymnasium would slip back into that indifferent and aimless period when the last Olympiad has gone by and the next is far ahead.

The Pletrion was separated from the other sports fields by a courtyard with a well, behind which was a small garden in full bloom round a deep reservoir. A man was drawing water and sprinkling it over the garden-beds. At sight of the intruders he shouted:

"Keep on the footpath and don't trample the flowers."

Heeding his warning, they walked in single file, carefully, along the narrow brick-paved path through this curious part of the world which no one had imagined existed behind the wall of their busy hum.

The Pletrion, a quadrangle with sides a hundred feet in length, was enclosed by a wall which had an abundance of niches in it for benches or statues. Effigies of Heracles, Hermes, Apollo, the patrons of athletic youth, smiling in stone, were modelled on the lines of ancient sculptural art. On the walls were numerous inscriptions, many of them already worn and faded. Those who formerly exercised here had carved on them their names and places of origin, often adding some witty remark, and always the name of the event. One came across names long-forgotten and already legendary. It was difficult to realise that one could touch the spot where the palms of the gigantic Lygdamis, of Polymestor who had caught a hare in the field, of the imperishably famous Milon of Kroton had rested.

This was the oldest part of the gymnasium, the most ancient athletic arena, reminiscent of the times of the first Olympiad. The impressive smallness of this famous field was like that of a miniature world within a fixed horizon which did not encroach upon the frontiers of Elis. The whole site—from the cracks in the wall which had never been mended to the grey sand which looked as if the ashes of ages had powdered it—seemed to be a precious remnant, a sacred relic.

All moved about very quietly. They walked beside the wall, stood before the statues and read the inscriptions. Sotion craned his head at all angles to pick out the letters which the great Chionis of Sparta had inscribed and by which he was remembered. Running from right to left, the letters followed each other, slanting downward, and Sotion had to squat to read the end of the inscription. But the writing broke off at the fissure in the wall, from which a tuft of grass had grown out.

To start with, they were at a loss as to what should be done. For over a score of people, differing so widely in their sporting objective, a hundred square feet were of no great use. Among the wrestlers, pancratiasts and boxers some ideas were suggested, but these were soon abandoned. Epharmostos bent down and dug up a lump of sand with his hand.

"It is well beaten down," he remarked.

Their bodies, accustomed to uninterrupted movement, began to weaken with this inactivity.

"One may as well sit down," said Sotion, not altogether certain whether or not this was in order under the rules governing this spot.

He selected a bench wedged into a deep niche. Here was a pleasant shade which might almost be called cool. A plane-tree growing beyond the wall stretched its stately boughs over to this side. Gradually everybody gathered here and, some sitting and others lying or standing, formed a clumsy group of idleness, somnolence and boredom.

Sotion, looking from his dark corner at the sandy stretch in the bright, scorching heat, asked as if out of the blue:

"Does Helios hold his shield in his hand or is it slung on his shoulder?"

"In his left hand," answered Gerenos.

"That is not a shield," says Skamandros, "but a wheel."

"The wheel of a chariot? So he drives on a single wheel?"

"No. The second one, on the other side, is hidden from view."

"He sets out from Ethiopia, where he has a golden house."

"Not a house, only a cave. A vault of crystal," corrected Gerenos.

"In the evening he bathes in the Ocean at the garden of the Hesperides."

"And when does he return?"

"At night he crosses the Ocean from west to east."

Agesidamos's eyelids drooped like a child's which has heard its fairy-tale and is ready to fall asleep. However, he overcame his drowsiness:

"By boat?"

"No, in a golden bowl."

Ergoteles after a pause said:

"When I sailed here from Himera there was a man on the ship who told these things differently."

"Can you tell me, son of Philanor," interposed Telesikrates, "who it was?"

"I don't know. A clever man, such was my impression. He came from somewhere on the coast, from Croton or from Metapontum. He explained——"

Ergoteles hesitated, then continued in an undertone:

"According to him, Helios does not ride across the heavens. 'Like other gods,' he asserted, 'Helios does nothing. He lives in happiness and does not toil so terribly. But we keep moving unceasingly.'"

"How is that: we?" murmured some of them.

"We, that means the earth. The earth, the sun, the moon and all the stars spin, rushing on perpetually."

"The earth moves?" Pataikos was awe-stricken.

Gryllos, too, did not understand, but he reckoned that the incomprehension of the Boeotian was incomparably worse.

"Don't be afraid, she won't run away from you."

"That man knew how to explain it," said Ergoteles. "You are born in this perpetual motion, he affirmed, and you die in the same motion, hence you don't notice it. And so on and so forth, but I just can't remember. He called it a dance. All the heavenly bodies, as it were, linked hands and whirled round an altar. This altar is the fire, the great burning core, which we do not see. From it comes light, warmth and life to the earth, the sun and all the stars."

97

Silence prevailed. Each one is inclined at one moment
to agree and at another to contradict. But meanwhile
through the door of their minds, slightly ajar, there
entered the faint breath of this unintelligible idea.
Hearth, altar—thus the cosmos takes on the familiar
shape of a house within which a feast is being celebrated.
The young couple—the earth and sun—together with the
wedding guests circle round the altar, and all of them
kindle their torches at the maternal hearth. This new
thought, disquieting at first, calms them because of its
notion of a melodious harmony. Governed by the sublime
rules of nature through which their bodies are kept perfectly poised, they feel safe and sure as the cosmos itself,
the movement of which continues independent of man's
hypotheses.

The hum of the gymnasium continued, compressed,
dense, unbroken, beyond the borders of this fragment of
quiet. But in that clamour, though it was all of a piece,
like a metal bar, their expert ears distinguished all the
overlapping voices. Each arena echoed differently. But at
times a particular pitch was wanting. This formed a
chasm of silence in a landscape filled with a wild uproar.
At these moments someone remarked: "They are finishing the jumps" or "Aipytos has interrupted the bout."

A pleasant laziness environed them. The consciousness of other people's exertion, the incessant rhythm of
work, made them fully realise the saturated sweetness
of rest.

However, the gymnasium, until now like an open
parchment, every letter of which speaks at once, began
to roll up. The Sacred Track, the Tetragonon, the Soft
Field, grew quiet in turn and were mantled by a faint

unintelligible murmur. "What has happened?" Sotion gave the lead by rising abruptly.

An incident which broke the whole routine of the day had occurred on the sacred track. Onomastos, the hellanodikes who was directing the practices with the discus, ordered Ikkos's throw to be measured. A slave did so, with a spear five feet in length. The throw measured nineteen spears, the last count falling exactly at the throw, not so much as a finger's width out. Said Onomastos:

"That is Phayllos's throw."

Had he mentioned only the distance—ninety-five feet —it would have been simply accepted, but as he backed it with the hero's name the matter took on prodigious proportions.

Phayllos of Croton had won the championship in Delphi in three events, once in running and twice in the pentathlon. He achieved this in about his twentieth year, so could count on a brilliant future. At the seventy-fifth Olympiad the olive wreath was predicted for him. Indeed, he had already prepared to set out on the journey, but war broke out. What did Phayllos do? He sold his fields and his house, which had been awarded to him by the town, borrowed more money from his friends, bought a ship, recruited volunteers and was the only one from the whole Italian coast to go to the help of the homeland. At Salamis, however, he perished.

Sotion and his comrades found the gymnasium so changed that they felt as if they had been away for a year. Though they numbered a score or so, each of them was of some consequence. But here they stood on the stadium and felt that their importance had diminished infinitely. The stadium, like a see-sawing plank, was tilting over to the full on Ikkos's side. Pataikos clapped his hands:

"The very first day, when I saw him with that fish, I knew there would be trouble with him."

Once more they were obliged to look on at all the "Tarentine eccentricities", at the unintelligible order of his exercises, his whims with the food, the heating of the water, the sight of the servitor bustling around him. The variety of his eager activities could, indeed, shake the most stable equilibrium. Having emerged from the crowd in which they had formerly lost him, he now did not drop out of their sight. Even when he was not in view, an annoying prickle would irritate their backs and, on turning round, they would meet the glance of Ikkos, unruffled and observant.

"What does he see in us?" snarled Eutelidas.

And Sotion answered: "Lungs, heart, muscles, tendons, bones, cartilages. I feel transparent whenever he looks at me."

"It is worth while observing him too," said Epharmostos. "Yesterday he was in the Tetragonon, I watched him wrestling. He was very strange."

Indeed Ikkos behaved at times like an expert, while at other moments he seemed a mere fumbler. He knew all the holds; their time-honoured names he knew by heart; he defined them by the names of the gods, the heroes and the famous athletes; he quoted rules from the different Games; but on many occasions Eurymenes found fit to advise him that he would do better to write a book on this subject and not take up wrestling as an amusement. Ikkos scarcely ever did anything more than defend himself. There were moments, however, when he was bewildering. The eye was unable to follow the lightning speed with which he broke loose from the most vigorous hug. But at once he would falter. He would go into a daze and fail to recognise the obvious opening that offered. "Is he blind or does he pretend to be?" One was never sure.

But what was most unbearable was that the gymnasium now appeared to be a house of mirrors. Ikkos's manner and actions were imitated on all the training grounds so precisely that it seemed he had reproduced himself indefinitely, with only the face changed into a boyish, a bearded, a white or a dark one. The indifference of the hellanodikai was astounding. Did they not notice it? In what gymnasium would it be permitted? Everything was going awry. Obviously people were neglecting the regular routine. From time to time someone would disappear and, except for Eutelidas, who alone could tell where the truant was lurking, it was impossible to trace him.

The Spartan was vexed. This laxity of discipline irritated him. Nurtured in the spirit of barrack-room comradeship, he rebelled against this new influence that was beginning to hold sway over the practice grounds.

"You, that Hysmon is so fond of," he said to Sotion, "you tell him how they decamp to the courtyard once his back is turned. No one does even half of the set exercises."

Sotion merely shrugged his shoulders:

"Mind your own business."

Time, the inflexible power, engulfed Sotion and his group. Over and over again, in a different way, they became aware of its agency. They arose before dawn and the day drove them headlong onwards. Towards the evening they stood panting and dead-beat at the well, gazing at the retreating daylight as if it were the last setting of the sun. Furthermore, it seemed to them that the months they had spent here had been surprisingly short in comparison to the time still on hand, which, though it was actually ebbing away fast, seemed still to stretch out over a long and commodious interval. They felt that all the exercises could still be accomplished and this roused an aspiring self-confidence in them. The door seemed wide open for some unheard-of and salutary change.

But the incredible happened: these irritating moments of suspense produced in Sotion's circle what would be termed a revolt in an escort of bodyguards or a civil war in a beleaguered city. The spectre of Ikkos was already appearing round every corner.

Skamandros tarried in the Pletrion as much as he could.

"After all, it was specially opened as a place to relax in."

Dandis seconded him:

"I am entered for the diaulos only and I don't see why I should go through all the exercises like a boy in a palestra, the more so since nobody insists on my doing it."

Epharmostos blurted out:

"Sotion is childish. He likes to chase after work all day long when the sun is scorching."

Menalkes added: "I have two or three bouts a day and I consider that amply sufficient. Aipytos does not demand any more. If Sotion likes to amuse himself, let him do so. Are there not enough boys here?"

But Sotion could not reckon on the boys. Ikkos's scientific dexterity had dazzled their trainers, who were brooding on their charges like anxious hens. In no other gymnasium until now was there heard so often: "Don't tire yourself!" "Don't touch the discus, you have nothing to do with that." "Don't jump about after a meal, wait until you are called for." And from dawn to dusk they subjected their pupils to such a series of massages that many of them could hardly stand up afterwards.

This was ridiculous and lamentable. Uncertain thoughts lined their foreheads, those foreheads that had been so smooth and void of suspicion. They were tormented by their want of enlightenment, they would have liked to explain matters to themselves but words failed them, and their distressed souls were betrayed by inapposite gestures.

Sotion was startled to realise how much this was affecting him. For some months he had lived under the same roof and had engaged in bouts with them, he had shared the same bread and the same hopes. He had considered himself no whit better or worse than any one of them—to be brief, he had pursued, as he thought, a course parallel to those they had taken. But it was now apparent that his track had led in a circle and that all the rest were its radii. Leader? This word had no meaning within these walls, no one would have thought of uttering it, no one would have thought of laying it at anybody's feet.

But, above all, one secret had been revealed, the heart

had removed its mask. It now lay defenceless as on an open palm. All that was most praiseworthy in them was not the outcome of their heritage or of an enthusiasm which was common to them all, or even of a desire to win. It had its origin in quite another quarter, it was the result of their state of excitement or of an unexpected power which no one could count upon. One accepted another's effort as one's own. A comrade's achievement was a thing to be proud of, it engendered an elevating sensation. Mutual affection, to some extent a surrender to a melting mood, had been for all a source of stimulation, perseverance and defiance. Such was this fierce affinity—of a score or so of bodies like those of the others—which distinguished them from the jumble in the gymnasium.

And he, Sotion, the ephebe, with no right to direct those of maturer years, found himself in the very centre of the circle because he was endowed with a fervour surpassing theirs.

Indeed he nourished them on his own life, he gave them their fill of his ecstasy, he incited them with the exultation which he himself derived from each of their triumphs. Were they to overlook in their reckoning of time all the moments when he had inspired them, there would remain only colourless days of effort and routine. Vowed to no aim and singularly unencumbered, he shone like a strayed fragment of the Golden Age giving out the gleam of his happy and purposeless life. In him was impersonated the spirit of the Games: the pleasant service of the gods to whom were offered up the redoubled rhythm of the heart, the straining of the muscles and the body dripping with sweat, as the music of the flutes, the crackling of the fire and the blood of the slain animal are offered up on an altar.

Such matters were never discussed among them; they were self-evident. Sotion expressed them by each of his actions, in which there was neither reflection nor economy. He spent himself, unconcerned about the resources of his youthful strength, and the perfection which he attained was not the result of deliberate thought, but, to put it briefly, a favour of the gods in compensation for a decent and sincere sacrifice. The affection with which they surrounded him and in which they themselves found a most lively encouragement was nothing but the assent accorded by their Hellenic souls to the ideal implanted by their fathers and forefathers.

But suddenly they were sundered by misgiving. There came among them the man whom they had ridiculed and rejected, but who stood out on his own like a stone in a brook. Everything now divided into separate ripples; tiny foaming eddies were formed. Sotion, never having experienced any condition other than the calm serenity that usually pervaded him, felt for the first time in his life the bitterness of a discord within himself. Ikkos irritated him, disquieted and alarmed him. The appearance of this friend of his childhood made such an impression on him that it seemed he had come across a stranger's footprint on the edge of his world.

That world of his lost its stability and Sotion now moved, as it were, on shaking and uncertain ground. Courage failed him and at moments he had such a dejected feeling that his one desire was to disappear, to slide down from this hot eminence and lose himself in the dismal ineffectual life of the mediocre set.

Sodamos said to Gryllos—in a dialect of the coast whence they both came:

"Sotion is sailing under furled canvas."

This went on for a few days, until suddenly on a certain afternoon Sotion equalled the "throw of Phayllos". Here was eloquence befitting these sunny sands! His disc, like an inspired word, recalled those who were near to breaking away. So, with a strong and stirring new watchword, a leader infuses fresh life into his army about to collapse in the desert. And as if Sotion had broken down some barrier, they all began to advance. Sodamos went a palm's breadth further and Eutelidas fell barely two feet short of them. Thus the chain which bound them in the pentathlon began to link up bit by bit until "Sotion's circle" became again a complete unit.

In all this Ikkos had a share which was not to be forgotten. "Phayllos's throw" remained his undisputed triumph. It was covered with esteem, like the ancestor of a line of illustrious descendants. Whatever else might be said about this man, undoubtedly to him they owed the day that marked a new era in the history of the gymnasium. For himself he advanced no further, but—as they all realised—he never lost ground. Ever steadfast, he clung to his legitimate gains. The breach was healed through their common struggles with him.

Kallias, the pancratiast, announced before the whole pentathlon set:

"This is an opponent worth meeting."

An opponent, certainly. . . . But when they regained their balance, when no one any longer "sought salvation in Tarentum", as this unusually vacillating and anxious period was described, Ikkos found himself wellnigh in his old position, plunged in scathing ridicule. It was impossible for them to overcome their antipathy towards his method of living. He alienated them by his audacious and fervent desire to revolutionise everything. He would have constructed the gymnasium on different lines, he would have planted the trees in a different pattern, he would have introduced other periods for rest, exercise and meals; the day, the rich day of the gods, would have run out as drops of water in the water-clock. In the midst of all this reckoning and reasoning there would be hardly any time to live.

"To live?" said Ikkos. "A slave can do that for you."

"My dear fellow, I won't agree to being replaced by a slave in that," objected Sotion.

Ikkos replied with a nasal hollow-toned chuckle:

"Splendid, splendid! I would not allow myself to be replaced either, but I live by my muscles."

Everybody recoiled as if in the Tarentine's stead they saw another man whom no one knew.

CHAPTER VIII

ALL this happened in the Pletrion, to which Ikkos had long attached himself.

"This place seems as if it were meant just for him," remarked Eutelidas, when Ikkos was first seen there.

Indeed, the Tarentine occupied it with the preciseness peculiar to him. He straightway chose the best bench, diligently searched out a dried stump of a root in the niche on which he hung his oil vessel, and placed his scraper and towels within easy reach of his hands. He was the only one who made use of the Pletrion not merely for meal times and rest periods but also for private training. Where he produced fresh sand from, no one could tell.

And now, when all had finished their cheese and fruit, he had not yet started to eat. He was waiting for the exact moment when he would have cooled down after his exercises and might eat without harm to his health. He sat in his shady niche, as comfortable as possible, with a towel over his back in order to avoid touching with his bare body—which was it?—either the roughness or the chill of the wall. After those unusual words, his piercing glance hovered above them like that of a hawk hovering in empty space.

"What has frightened you all so much?"

He unwrapped his portion from its fig-leaves and began eating. He looked at them quizzically now, evidently amused at their embarrassment.

"Go on, start, Melesias, start telling them what was uppermost in my mind. We are both of the same profession. I am a gymnastic instructor the same as you. Are you not paid for training Timasarchos here to be a wrestler?"

"I earn my livelihood through my knowledge, and not by the employment of my body."

"Yes, you are right. Though you are dressed, I can see that your body would not keep you. I am, however, still hoping to get something for my legs and shoulders."

"What does that actually mean: to live by one's muscles?" asked Pataikos meekly.

"Blessed be Boeotia!" roared Ikkos. "They say it is a country of dull people, but of all this company you are the first to put a sensible question. Listen, it means that I am practising because I want to be strong and skilful and I hope that it will bring in my daily bread."

"A morsel of bread? Is that why you are going to Olympia?" asked Sodamos.

"For nothing else. The Olympian olive is sufficiently nourishing, isn't it?"

They looked at each other in amazement. This essentially concrete notion seized hold of them; everyone pictured only a twig with some grey leaves, and the sapless rustle of this withered relic created a void in their minds. Simultaneously an oppression descended on them, the air had become vitiated. Sodamos rubbed his hand across his forehead:

"I always thought so," he murmured.

Ikkos, however, was living that day in a cloudless atmosphere:

"Gryllos, at your town during the Panathenaia, pitchers filled with olive-oil are awarded to the champions. These can be sold for some money in return. But were you to get the wreath in Olympia, tell us how much is prescribed by Solon's law to be paid out by the treasury?"

"Five hundred drachmæ," retorted the Athenian.

"See, you will then be wealthy."

"I never gave it a thought."

"Maybe. But I think of such trifles."

"And don't forget to call in at Argos sometime. At our place wonderful things of bronze are to be won," shouted Dandis.

"And at our place a silver goblet!"

"I have heard of a warm cloak at Pellene!"

From everywhere similar cries were forthcoming. Ikkos stretched his hands out as if he were gathering in what was thrown to him.

"Yes, go on, go on. And Xenophon? Aren't you going to give me anything?"

"Why should I?" Xenophon asked, taken aback.

"Well, you are the son of the famous Thessalos. What did your father do during his lifetime? Did he not go to all the Games? Did he not gather some hundreds of prizes?"

The boy reddened deeply and glanced pitiably around. Ergoteles, who was standing beside him, caressed his flowing locks:

"Don't worry. You have nothing to be ashamed of."

Ikkos lifted a piece of cheese to his mouth, chewed it thoroughly and swallowed it:

"You are children, all of you, from Glaukos whose beard is only just commencing to sprout, up to Gerenos who is already going grey at the temples. You keep looking at me as if I were a werewolf because I voice openly what each one of you thinks silently."

"Don't meddle with our thoughts," growled Sodamos.

"Very well! Why, from the first day you set me so far from yourselves that I could touch neither your thoughts nor your bodies except in a bout."

"That is your own fault," remarked Sotion.

"You laughed at me as if I were a buffoon in a fair."

"And what else are you?" inquired Gerenos.

The serious tone of this question angered Ikkos:

"What, Hairy, must I tell you that I noticed how your ignorance fell from you bit by bit; how Eurymenes rolled you on the sand like a stone? You learnt wrestling from the elephants."

"Enough! Enough!" Kallias admonished him. "Your chatter merely irritates us."

"Since when does one talk in Athens with the fist?"

Never before had Ikkos had so much the upper hand over them. It was impossible to defeat him with any argument. He was intolerably rude and derisive. But suddenly he astonished them:

"I am poor," he said.

Many thought they had heard wrong. What does he mean, this man whose athletic physique covers his nudity? But others, who had grown up esteeming money, understood that poor means wicked, iniquitous, prone to commit any offence. To them Ikkos turned:

"Be careful though, don't be prejudiced! Remember what Simonides of Keos says about a certain Olympic victor: that he formerly carried fish from Argos to Tegea. Had I not learnt gymnastics when I did, I should have had to do something of that sort too. And I say boldly that I mastered it better than anyone else. It is only you who consider it buffoonery."

He shook off the crumbs of cheese that remained on his thigh, covered his back again with his towel and pressed himself against the cool wall. Everybody kept silent as if absorbed in lazy afternoon musing.

"You think too much of yourself," Kallias declared. "Why should we concern ourselves about what you do?"

"No one asked you to. But one would have thought that such competitors would have some knowledge of gymnastics."

"By Zeus! Perhaps it was you who invented gymnastics?"

"Son of Didymos, you were born rich. From early life, you have never tried to think where all these things come from which you use. Food, the bed you sleep on, the garment you wear, these beautiful scrapers, one of which you lost and didn't even think of searching for it, your house—though probably you have more than one—all this you just take for granted as you take the air. You have slaves for everything and even here there are two aleiptai to serve you. Others have toiled that you might be what you are. You acquired your skill and the deftness of your fists like a ready-made chiton, and you have no idea who collected the flax for it, who wove it, or who sewed it."

"I suppose you'll say I learnt gymnastics with my arms folded?"

"That's certain. You'll be told that all right," interrupted Telesikrates. "He must think us a lot of rabbits!"

"Oho!" exclaimed Ikkos. "You, son of Karneades, you set an example of diligence to us all. You draw your plough uphill. You were born to be a wrestler, but instead you are entered for the running. That really looks like heroism—which, by the way, Hysmon ought to knock out of your head or from wherever it has got into you, for I can't appeal to your common sense, not knowing where that is."

A smile brings people together. This momentary contraction of the risible muscle, which changes a few lines in the features of a face, is often enough equal to a treaty of peace. Ikkos's last words carved on some people's faces only a faint arch round the lips and created tiny wrinkles at the outer corners of their eyes, while on others' faces it even raised the upper lip to show the teeth and narrowed the eyelids. The Tarentine did not abuse the advantage which this moment of gaiety had conferred on him, but said frankly:

'I had to fend for myself early in life. It was then that I learnt to care about everything and gymnastics too seemed to me worth attention. I realised that our palestras and gymnasiums ought to give us more than they do."

"They were good enough for greater people than we are, and so they ought to be good enough for us," interrupted Sodamos.

"I am not astonished an Arcadian should talk like that. But in your parts, just as in our Tarentum, people from childhood onwards look only at the sea and never towards the heart of the country. The sea moves but the land remains unchanged. What I think is this; the land is that which has been, but the sea is the future, new and fresh. What has been no one can alter any more, there is no need even for any alteration, whether it was bad or good. But that which is before us we can change as we wish to."

"It must be as the gods will," said Gerenos.

"Gryllos, tell him the Athenian proverb: call on Athena, but bestir yourself also."

Gryllos nodded, quite pleased.

"Yes, my Naukratian," said Ikkos, "the gods would be soon tired were we to seek their protection for everything. Why implicate the gods? I don't think I have ever offended them. On the contrary, nothing would please them more than for man to aim at a definite perfection. Who can tell, had I your strength, perhaps I should be contented, but my body was never classed with the best in the palestra. You remember, Sotion?"

"Nor mine either," replied the ephebe.

"Ah! Yes, truly," and he stared at him for so long that it seemed his thoughts were elsewhere.

Unconsciously everybody turned towards Sotion. He seemed now to have grown in size and looked more mature. And this was no illusion, for they had always seen him when he was on the move and they themselves were engaged in their strenuous routine. At times his body had attracted their attention through some new detail, it had seemed then that an invisible chisel had moved along his contours. Thus, for instance, the better developed muscles of the back made up for the unshapeliness of the spine, which recently had stood out as it does in boys. The whole frame, however, no one had marked, and not till this moment, when he stood motionless, were they struck by the full exuberance of his fresh beauty.

"Yes, such a body is worthy of praise," said Ikkos. And with the same breath but in an undertone: "Reared up in such improvidence."

"You wouldn't have dared?" laughed Sodamos.

"You wanted to wound me, but you guessed rightly. I wouldn't dare to leave everything to nature."

"You would have too much to lose."

"Don't let us quarrel about it. When I tell you that I have thought about gymnastics, I don't mean to say that I personally invented all that which in me astonishes you so much. Do you know that Milon wrote a book on the subject? You may laugh, Philon. But it's so far to Tyras that probably only your great-grandson will get there to read this book. All the same, it would be of use to you too. You would find therein the advice that a wrestler should eat meat once a day."

"The Olympic rules don't say anything about that."

"My dear fellow, the Olympic rules belong to times when there were no other contests in Olympia except the foot-races. Besides, do they prescribe anything about food? You are given, as of old, cheese and dried figs, but if anyone wants to eat something different, he is at liberty to do so. Till now I did not understand why that fish which was brought for me the first day perturbed you so much."

This remark was addressed to all of them, but the answer came from Gryllos:

"If you could have looked at yourself then, you would have laughed too. What competitor, having scarcely entered the gymnasium, takes so much care of his stomach?"

"Then what, my Athenian, should a competitor care for, if not for his body? What would you say of a lute-player who left his harp anywhere and did not care for it until the strings are eaten up by rust? The body is our instrument and we ought to treat it well, so that our playing may attain perfection."

Someone sighed and others shuffled impatiently. The sand on which they were sitting began to prick them. Skamandros got up, stretched his limbs and yawned as a dog does. Sotion left his place near the wall, took a few steps, and bending in the form of a splendid bow took up a handful of sand from the ground of the arena. He allowed it to run out slowly from his closed fist; later he opened his palm and studied the remaining grains as if he were counting them. Finally he shook them off and wiped his hand on his hip.

"This competitor of yours, Ikkos," he said, "smells like bed."

All heads turned towards him, and standing there in the glaring sunlight his broad and oil-smeared chest reflected the light so dazzlingly that it made them blink.

"Why so?"

"By Heracles! When I listen to you and think of this competitor who should take so much care about himself, it appears to me that I see a quiet, half-darkened room, I hear the spoon being cautiously stirred in the medicine-glass. It is evident that this competitor of yours needs peace. The sun is scorching him and he can't get enough sleep. He needs food which has been measured out. He is worried by a loss or an excess of weight. In many things, very many things, about which no one pays any attention, which one takes without question like the air taken into the lungs, he sights danger. He consults physicians or he is his own physician—didn't you once tell us that for a sprinter an enlarging spleen was dangerous and that there are infusions of herbs which one ought to drink in order to avoid this?"

"Certainly," agreed Ikkos. "Who says our profession does not demand sacrifices?"

Sotion raised his hand:

"There is no profession of athletes!"

"Is there not? Are you sure?" Ikkos gave a hollow guttural laugh. "Astylos. . . ."

This name was repeated in a general murmur. Astylos of Croton was the most brilliant athlete of the day. In the last three Olympiads, in the stadium, in the diaulos and in the hoplite-race he had won seven wreaths. To cast a slur on such fame was iniquity.

"You are a wicked man," yelled Gryllos.

"Don't forget"—Ikkos raised his voice too—"that for a number of years I have lived in Croton. And you can see that I keep my eyes wide open. But as this offends you, I will not say anything more. You will be convinced for yourselves in Olympia."

"Will Astylos be there this year?"

"He will, and if I am not mistaken he will not disappoint you."

Again they lost touch with him. The conversation drifted into obscure and tortuous side-tracks. There was no doubt but that Ikkos knew his way round and was always at a point from where all of them could be seen grouped together as in an open field. He disappeared, however, every now and then, hiding himself behind words; whereupon they took again their former dislike to this man who seemed to them stranger than ever. Many were inclined to get up and go away, but they remained seated opposite him as if on the other side of a gulf. The feeling of strangeness was so real that it startled them when they heard his voice, quite natural though it was, breaking the stillness:

"If you are offended by the word profession, let us call it art. I don't suppose any of you denies that running, the pentathlon or wrestling is an art? We are acquiring it, but all have not the same abilities. The days when Glaukos of Karystos could pass straight from the plough to become a boxer have gone."

"But, as he won some wreaths, things did not turn out badly for him," intimated Menalkes.

"Yet you did not follow his example? I beg of you, let us not talk like children. Here we are, more than a score of able athletes, everyone has passed through the palestra, then the gymnasium, this and that one has succeeded in finding an aleiptes or a gymnast to keep on training him, and finally you have arrived here, where, they say, the best school is, and day after day each one exercises as much as he can, and knows——"

"But you are overstepping the mark," interrupted Sotion.

"What mark?"

"The Athletic Ideal."

These words fell on them like a radiant beam and all

their dislike for this enigmatic fellow found a dazzling explanation. Their minds, undecided on matters that were concealed in the depth of foreboding and in their subconscious impulses, had been harassed by all these disputes. These were now merged in the blurring dusk. The truth was so near that many checked the exclamation of astonishment on their half-opened lips: how was it that they had not perceived it earlier?

"You talk of us as if we were alone in the world. But behind us there are thousands whom the same dawn awakens to the practices and whom the same dusk accompanies on their return from the gymnasiums."

"Our proficiency is an encouragement and an example for them."

"I think so too, but what example can you set to all those who never diverge from their ordinary life, whom fate does not lead on our path? Why should you want to give them a body which makes endless demands and is full of whims? Why drill them into an exaggerated cautiousness? For what benefit should they surround themselves with care like a precious statuette in a wooden box? Really, one would imagine they were fragile things liable to be shattered or damaged."

"And what would you have them do?"

"Nothing, I would leave them where they are in those gardens of gaiety and freedom, the palestras and gymnasiums which our ancestors built through the favour of the gods. I am one of those too, only I differ from them in that a happy fate allowed me to proceed to Olympia—a happy fate, nothing else."

Ikkos did not interrupt. He kept looking at him with a glance so dark that it seemed the entire gloom of the niche in which he was sitting had gathered under the arch of his meeting eyebrows. Sotion saw him but dimly.

"You hide the competitors until the show proper. You adorn them with the strength and skill necessary only for the short moment of display. That is why I claim that you are over-stepping the mark. A competitor such as you wish to model would by no means represent ideal lustihood, but rather be an example of useless strength, useless for life, demanding active attention and protection as weakness does. You talk of self-denial; I don't want to deny myself anything. How I would regret, on later reflection, that I had not given my body its full scope, that in the prime of my life I did not do all I could for it."

He ceased speaking but still quivered with the cry from the heart. He felt the animated gaze of his comrades upon himself, and this spurred him on.

"I loathed you as I would an overseer of slaves, when those poor people on whom you imposed your will kept dancing around you. You shackled their power. I care not for what you eat or when you sleep, though I suppose one could learn a few good points from you, but you want to fetter us. And after that it would not be permissible to breathe without first thinking 'Is this the moment for a short breath or for a long one?' Behind you trails a faint-hearted anxiety, a stupid cowardice unknown to men until now, a dread of every redundant or unpremeditated movement. You watch over your body as if it were a full amphora to be carried, untouched, right up to Olympia without spilling a drop. Your ambition has enslaved you.'

"And you"—Ikkos hawked as if clearing some obstruction from his throat—"are you not concerned in the least? Not even to be the best?"

"To be the best, yes," exclaimed Sotion. "That is enough in itself."

"Do you mean it does not expect any reward? Even if renown be the reward?"

"Renown? That's as if you said heaven!"

"So furiously did you snatch yourself off the earth that, if I did not follow you at once, I may be pardoned."

"For aught one knows, you would never be able to reach so far by your own strength," shouted Sodamos.

Ikkos got up and emerged from his niche. He flung the towel which covered his back on to the bench. This piece of cloth, always folded with such an irritating exactness, so symmetrically four-square, never spoiled by any rucks, now lay crumpled, disarranged in gathers and wrinkles, a very ruin of peace and harmony.

Ikkos set out tramping along the opposite wall, as if he were taking his afternoon walk. The faint scrunch of sand accompanied his equal paces. They sounded like a graduation of time, a needless counting of moments which died away into serene calm. Sotion's friends were perched now, as it were, on the edge of a bowl of uniform brightness which was transparent throughout its depth to the golden bottom. Their thoughts rocked as boats do when oars are at rest.

Suddenly the neighing of horses was heard. It came from somewhere close by; the animals must be standing just outside the stadium. In a trice all were on their feet. The youths paled from excitement.

The horses had arrived already! As the crowing of

cocks in the night announces the coming day, so the neighing of horses brought to those in the gymnasium the first sign that the season of the practices and trials was nearing its end. The horses make their appearance at the beginning of the last month. They are inspected and, once registered on the racing list, depart for Olympia.

Everybody from the Pletrion dashed off to the Agora. In the centre stood a team of horses. From their hoofs covered with bast wrappings, and from the white dust clinging to their hides, it was clear that they had just arrived from a great distance. Ergoteles said:

"They are Sicilian horses."

"How do you know?"

"I recognise Hieron's men."

And he pointed out the servants, the keepers of the horses and the grooms of the stable, all of whom had silver epaulets marked with the monogram of the Syracusan tyrant. They busied themselves around their animals, leading them in turn to the hellanodikes, who investigated their age, scrutinised them with a quick glance and wrote down their names on an earthen tablet.

The whole of this ceremony was watched by the townspeople who, catching sight of the competitors, greeted them with shouts. Immediately a swarm surged on all sides of them and they were surrounded by looks of admiration. A few of those who were bolder pressed forward to feel their bodies. A wave, more spirited, captured Sotion and carried him off.

"See what they are doing to him!" exclaimed Sodamos.

But Gerenos had already run and pushed the people aside. He snatched up the youth and bore him out of the crowd on his shoulders. Sotion slung his leg on the giant's shoulder, clambered up and sat astride his neck, like a young Dionysos riding on a hairy Seilenos.

CHAPTER I

IT is the third new moon after the summer solstice.
This nocturnal beacon is carried across the whole
extent of the Greek world by the great arch of the
heavenly vault stretched from the Caucasus to the Pil-
lars of Hercules. On the brow of the horizon Olympia
stands forth like a guiding star. From the woods, the
highlands and the sands of the coast, all the paths began
to thread their way out of the mountain defiles to the
open routes of the sea. To the gods watching on high they
must have seemed like yarns stretching from a spindle.
Numerous, scattered, tangled, they were gathered at last
into a few fibres running through the land of Elis.

The earliest stir was made on the road leading from
Dyme in Achaia. This joins in the neighbourhood of
Buprasion with that which brings visitors from the
western sea from the two ports, Hyrmine and Kyllene.

On each side of the beaten track, wheels creaked in
the deep ruts of roads where one vehicle could not pass
another. Alongside ran the bridle-path for pedestrians and for those who rode on horses, mules or asses.
There were processions, sacred *theoriai* sent by states
and towns, and in the train of these official representatives, the ordinary pilgrims. Provinces, tribes, towns,
communities kept together, and gaps could be picked

out between one party and another, between vehicles, riders and pedestrians. On occasion, when a wheel broke or an animal stumbled, the regular arrangement would be upset. The gaps would close up into a sudden disorder and ultimately the whole column would come to a stand-still raising a confused cry. The obstacle would be removed, while a crowd of laggards from all the various districts of the land gradually gathered. The vehicle needing repairs must go aside from the main path and could advance again only at the very end of the line.

The travellers made headway only at the sluggish pace of the bullocks which constituted the majority of the draught animals. Limbs flagged in the heat, the wayfarers were parched with thirst and the beasts cried out for water. At every rill a halt was made. Then the scene became livelier; youths would run with full buckets, cool goblets would be passed eagerly round from hand to hand. Some would undress themselves to lie for a while on the pebbles in the shallow stream and, possessed of a sudden vigour, would break out in song. Each time a wood or a heaven-sent clump of trees was reached, they would sit about in the shade, some playing on reed pipes, others handing round wine; and then, to overtake their parties, a fair stretch of the road would have to be made up at full speed.

Hats with wide drooping brims gave protection against the sun; but many wore leather caps and when these were removed a stream of sweat flowed from under them. For others a kerchief sufficed, which they fastened under the chin. Some had only the shade of their thick hair, which they wore long and had made into plaits. These were tucked away into linen bags and tied behind the head. The gentry from Sicily and Great Greece, reclining under parasols, drove in comfortable carriages, over some of which linen hoods were spread. At times, when these swayed, the long pale faces of old people who were weakened by the journey could be seen.

From noon onwards, impatience would increase; a quarrel would flare up over any trifle. The day dragged on as if it were never going to end and by the time evening arrived restlessness had embraced the whole column. Some would demand to settle down for the night while others noisily urged taking advantage of the cooler temperature to continue the journey. The bullocks, belaboured with whips, would thrust their horns into the bodywork of the vehicles in front of them. But ultimately fatigue would overcome them all, and surrounded by the neighing and braying of the horses and asses, the people would fall asleep often with an unfinished word on their lips. Unmindful, they would lie among the freshly tilled fields, on the stubble at the edges of the road which in the hours of dark while they slept became a clotted mass, and thus the dawn would find them, stilled as if by a magic spell.

At daybreak a distant bustle would set in. From far off, more vehicles would continue to arrive and demand the right of way. The sleepers would awake, stretching their stiffened limbs and in the sharp-scented air the sun would dry the dew from their garments.

In the environs of Elis temporary camps were pitched and others unceasingly took their place. No encampment was allowed to remain longer than one day, in order not to deprive later arrivals of room. Within the

bounds of the gymnasium numerous strangers began
to roam about. Searching for relatives, friends or acquaintances among the competitors. Kapros at last ordered
the gates to be shut, so that the exercises might not be
disturbed. Thereafter visitors were allowed into the hellanodikeon only, where they had to give particulars of the
athletes belonging to their communities.

The road further on climbed along the Akroreia
ranges in the direction of Oenoe, whose everlasting
maple-trees whispered the ancient stories of King
Augeas and his daughter, the enchantress who gathered
herbs on the banks of the Ladon. The merchants
paused for a few days in Aleision, where a fair was in
progress and the sick were attracted by the miraculous
springs of Herakleia gushing out below the temple of
the Ionic Nymphs. Beyond Salmona, the one-time
capital of Salmoneus, whom Zeus struck down with
lightning, the view over the plain of Olympia opened
out.

It lay in an angle between two rivers, for the broad
Alpheios was joined here by its tributary, the "murmuring" Kladeos. In the range of hills hemming the
plain, the steep city of Phrixa stood out. From its crest the
temple of the Kydonian Athena peeped from behind
trees, and on the hill the charred remains of wrecked
Pisa were still to be seen. Lastly Kronion, the hill of
Kronos, cast its pine-scented shadow over the sacred
circle which clung to its declivity. This was really a
grove, for the tops of the planes and the greyish
stocky olives could be distinguished, and above these
emerged the roofs of a few habitations. At one spot an
empty space with the mound of the smoking altar was

visible, and from here two golden, open strips branched out: the stadium and the hippodrome.

A deep calm, an enchanted placidity permeated every feature of this landscape. They who entered here for the first time stood pondering on the humble simplicity of Zeus's retreat. The Phokians, brought up in face of the awe-inspiring majesty of Delphi, scaled the heights, whence was disclosed still more widely the peace of the green valleys, the wooded ranges, 'the river flowing between its high myrtle-covered banks, lingering between its bends and watering the downy islands in its broad bed, until finally, in an endless expanse of light, it joined the glittering arc of the Ionian Sea. Such was the holy place of the deity, and as he himself had chosen the site, such must have been the peace of his soul too.

Meanwhile the human flood swelled about Olympia.

From the mouth of the Alpheios surged one wave which had been brought by the small ship now rocking at the shallow roadsteads; a second came from the north, from Elis; a third from Triphylia and Messenia in the south; and lastly a fourth from the east. This was the densest. It advanced along a great track traversing the whole of Arcadia from the sources of the Alpheios, which in the wildest parts of the mountains cuts this highway of migrating tribes. Linking up with it were all the roads from the eastern coast, from Laconia, from the Argolid, from Corinth, from Megara. To these again were joined those from remoter parts, from Attica, from Central Greece, and from all the islands of the Ægean, from Asia Minor and the Black Sea, from the harbours of Athens or Corinth, entered by many ships to avoid sailing right round the Peloponnesus. All these ways now met on the plain between the two rivers.

The vehicles, on arrival, stopped two stades away from the sacred circle. Here an empty space was marked out to enable the Olympic Council to make all the necessary arrangements.

From morn till night, the members of this Council, surrounded by rhabduchi and mastigophoroi (attendants armed with sticks), received the pilgrims. The first to appear were the architheoroi, the leaders of the processions. They notified the name of their community, the number of their followers, carriages and animals, and negotiated for a place to camp on. Of course, the nearest sites were the best. These were allotted to the states and towns most worthy of Olympia. A great deal could be achieved through the personal connections of the architeoros, but often he had to toil hard, running from one member of the Council to the other, imploring, arguing, appealing to his acquaintances, refreshing their memories of his identity, laying stress on an actual or a fictitious relationship which, if it could not be established among mortals, he would find among the deities and heroes of his country. Some nymph of his native district he would couple with the Olympian Zeus and from this union he would deduce his own lineage through a long line of ancestors, linking himself to some branch of this genealogy. Altercations arose if someone was assigned to a position a few stades away from Olympia. But this year even that could be looked upon as almost a privilege and it was advisable to occupy the site as soon as possible. Where the last arrivals would be installed it was difficult to imagine.

The separate groups moved forward, one by one, each accompanied by a member of the Council to ensure that the allotted boundaries of the locations should not be transgressed. This took up so much time that the roads became continuous encampments, embittered and quarrelsome. Not infrequently a whole day would be spent waiting and no passage through could be found until nightfall.

As in a dream, they entered the plain broidered with silvery light. Many, realising that they had reached their reservation at last, sat down on the ground with their hands clasped across their bent knees and gazed at the humble features of Olympia and listened to the dewy stillness while the animals, under yokes that had not yet been removed, lowed mournfully and nuzzled them with their wet nostrils.

Nobody retired till the moon had set. Thousands of eyes followed its brief course. Reflected in those eyes it lost its real shape, it seemed so simple and yet so inconceivable.

This goddess Selene appeared to some as having a golden diadem on her dark hair, to others it was a wreath of silver leaves or a flambeau with which she lit a way for herself through the night. Her eye was seen to possess a grey lustre, her cheek an immaculate whiteness, and a fringe of her forehead was visible through her half-opened veil. She was followed to her cave in the heart of the mountains or to somewhere about the bank of the stream which flows around the earth. She rode in a chariot, or was mounted on a bull, on a horse, a mule, or a white-fleeced ram.

This "goddess of many names" was born of the Titans

Hyperion and Theia, or, as some would have it, of Helios, who in some places was known as her brother, in others as her husband. She evaded human imagination like her own light, which scintillated among the waves of the sea in sparkling serpent coils. For many a chaste and immaculate virgin, at Nemea she was the mother of the monstrous lion; in Arcadia she was the beloved of the sylvan Pan; while those from Karian Herakleia knew of a certain cave on mount Latmos where every night she bends over Endymion, wrapped in perpetual sleep.

But here, in the land of Elis, whereof Endymion had been one of the first kings, Selene had borne him fifty daughters, the fifty months of the four-year cycle, the sacred interval of the Olympiad; and now, in the "virgin" month of Parthenios, her last daughter was nearing her fullness.

CHAPTER II

I N the river valley a gigantic and variegated settlement sprang up. Congested to the full in the
neighbourhood of the sacred circle, it became sparser
on the outskirts, although they too were becoming
more crowded every day. Circular tents, rectangular
tents, tents of leather or of linen in various colours
huddled together by communities, and each section was
separated from the other by a narrow lane. Inter-
related communities, however, kept together and these
larger divisions formed, as it were, whole countries—
Attica, Laconia, Boeotia, Sicily could be picked out and
thus a hundred boundaries of the Grecian world maintained their insularity in this press.

The charm of breaking bounds was, however, indulged
in. A Thespian, for instance, would set out in search
of an axe and, though he had one of his own in his tent,
he would fetch one from a Byzantine; a Messenian would
find his dog in distant Epeiros; the isle of Samos would
give Massalia water to drink. Something like a child's
desire was satisfied; Hermes's wings, as it were, grew on
one's feet and the world lost its vastness. At last all its
extremities could be visited and foreign countries could
be fully tasted.

Each encampment had a shape of its own. The order

of the tents, the arrangement of the carts, the site chosen for the rubbish dump—trivial details, although seemingly alike yet reflected the peculiarities of different regions. The characteristics of the mountains, the valleys and shores were reproduced in them; the beasts stretched their necks to this side and to that, as if they guessed the direction of their native byres and stables. Various climates clung to the people's garments. The Arcadians of the cold mountain heights would not discard their sheep-skins; round the bronzed nakedness of the inhabitants of Libya spread the desert where there is neither water nor rain, nor any dew. It was as if each one brought a little of the air of his own country, recognisable in the dissimilar odours of the tents. It came with the men and their implements; it emanated from the half-open tents, from the sawdust and rubbish to which the leaves, the blades of grass, the withered flowers that had been brought with the baggage had imparted their last breath. From the folds of a coat left a long time in the box, a butterfly would emerge, forsaking its cocoon that had been spun between the threads of the wool, to flutter in its alien colours like a spirit from a foreign country.

Variety of customs was reflected in every activity. Zones, latitudes and longitudes were mapped in human gestures, these revealed the existence of shepherds, husbandmen, merchants and mariners; the spit rotated in Spartan hands like a whizzing spear; the Argive sat on his stool as if on horseback; the woodman was recognised by his noiseless tread. But in spite of all these differences, Mother Greece seemed almost homogeneous amid the extraneous elements from the colonies. Africa, Iberia,

Gaul, Illyria, Italy, Scythia, Sarmatia, Syria, Egypt breathed from the depths of their mysterious history and civilisation upon those hundreds of Greek towns, that chain of minute links adhering to their shores. In the daily contact with barbarians, in the bustle of ports, during caravan journeys, impressions, prejudices, taints clung to a man, they penetrated the pores of the body like the dust of the street. The soul adorned itself with queer ornaments; the smile, the glance, a wave of the hand, gave expression, so it seemed, in terms of an unknown alphabet. Often, however, the knot on a cord or the shape of a pitcher, a tiny wrinkle or a quiver of the eyelids showing the last ripple of a deep and hidden storm of the feelings, was sufficient to reveal the amazing fraternal similarity which peeped out through these arabesques and cyphers.

In thousands of unforeseen ways they drifted apart and came together again. The language, broken up into innumerable dialects and provincialisms, and grown over with a foreign weed in the colonies, would bring about vexatious misunderstandings. An ordinary article, an instrument of everyday use would suddenly shroud itself in a mystery which for opposite extremes of the encampment it was impossible properly to unravel. The accents, the consonants, the aspirates, the genders were subject to inexplicable variations. Through the movements of the throat, the position of the mouth and the pressure of the teeth, even the vowels had changed so much that they could not be relied upon. In many cases there remained but the mere roots of words, just the core of the sounds to which their meanings had been committed by the ages that had slipped out of memory. But how quickly and eloquently these shoots had twined themselves into the ear and heart! Once they were grasped and understood they found their roots again, and spread into branches blooming with enormous bunches of foliage which cast a pleasant shade, that of distant lands and periods.

In the clear conception of fellowship there loomed the features of a bygone existence when all the tribes were still together, when a similar encampment, surrounded by the murmur of the northern steppes, weighed the thought of migrations and conquests. Where was that? When was it? No tradition, no myth gives any account of it. And yet there must have been a time when there were neither Dorians nor Aeolians nor Ionians, but one race held together by those bonds which now, once more, conveyed thoughts through all the lips' diversity of sound. Otherwise, whence comes this strange thread of warmth which binds every whisper of this miscellaneous gathering to the soul?

Many knew each other from previous Olympiads; companions of joint adventures found each other again; faces seen in distant ports, in courtyards under evening shades, returned to the memory; people whose homes lay in the remotest parts, who had once come across each other by chance, met again unexpectedly. Every few minutes vociferous welcomes burst forth.

"By Zeus! Whom do I see?"

"Perhaps you suffered a tempest again?"

"And what a tempest! I even heard the Sirens."

"Yes, yes, at our age we should do better to stay at home."

"No, it is horrible to imagine dying in the bed on which one first saw the light of day."

"What has age got to do with me?"

Everybody felt so young that to each of them the whole world seemed to bear the same fresh bloom as the girl who, yonder, moved about briskly in among the tents. She disappeared and from behind the linen flap only her voice was heard. Soft and floating it was like a golden sunbeam shed through all this masculine clatter, which all of a sudden ceased.

There was not a grown woman in the encampment. They remained at home, for the law did not permit them to enter the sacred grove during the season of the Games; they were not allowed even to cross the Alpheios. There, behind the river, towards Skillus, the Typaean rock is visible—whence it was decreed that offenders would be hurled down. As far back as human recollection went, this has never happened. The law was kept, though no one any longer knew how it originated. Some bias of the agricultural life in the dim ages had thrust the women aside that they might not sap the vigour meant for fruition; thrust them aside from the Olympian ceremonies for the same reason that it did not admit them to the cult of Eunostos of Tanagra, the patron of husbandry, and closed the temple of Kronos to them. Only young girls enjoyed the eternal privilege of their chastity.

Among these there was one whose name was on the lips of everybody in the encampment.

She walked about, leaning upon her father's arm. She was almost equal to him in height. The scanty Dorian peplos did not hide the lines of her body nor smother her figure in a superabundance of drapery. The young bloom of her shapely curves could be gauged through this piece of cloth which, gathered at the waist, hung in long parallel folds. Every pace threw these pleats open and beneath the soft wool a glimpse of the full and perfect leg was revealed. Broad in the shoulders, with bold breasts that swelled under the apoptygma covering them, the slenderness of her arms, her neck, and her feet peeping from their sandals announced to the world that her body was nourished by the sun of the coasts and the winds of the sea.

Born at Skione, on the Pallenian peninsula, Hydna accompanied her father, Skillus, on his sponge-seeking expeditions. From the rocks below the surface of the water with hands still half-childish she tore off these gelatinous living tufts, ever braver, more persevering in her combat with the sea and with the weight of the waves into which she plunged, ever quicker and more thorough in her work in the azure depth. Her lungs were capable of an unusually deep breath. The air, inhaled above water, would be held for so long that Skillus, who rose first to the surface, had each time to undergo the same trepidation and the same joy of relief. At last she would ascend. Her form would emerge for a moment above the water, panting with the strain on the lungs. Her chest would expand as if it were taking in the whole world and then, the next instant, with a flash of dazzling movement, she would become an integral part of the liquid element, and would continue so until she left the last wave at the shore.

Never did she imagine that her skill could serve for anything besides the catching of sponges. But then a war came, it approached like an eclipsing darkness, a human flood swept away their house, thousands of oars churned up the sea, their boat, tethered to an unknown ship, drifted with the north-eastern wind. There is no knowing how long they suffered in this violent turmoil. Earth and sky and sea resounded with tongues of which no noise resembled human speech. During this while all that Hydna made out was the one sentence: "Their anchors must be loosed." It was her father's voice, muffled and faint, and scarcely audible against the tempest's roar in the pitch-dark night.

And so their roving search beneath the waves began. They swam under the ships and crawled along the murky moving ooze until their hands encountered the cable. Then they shook the anchor loose and, tugging out its flukes wedged in the sea-bed, rose for breath to the surface where the hurricane, like a flash of lightning, burst into their lungs. The ship would lurch and be carried off in the gale. The frantic howling of the crew for a while added to the shrieking of the tempest, but at once they would dive again and yet another ship would be swept off into the abyss of the night. Thus they dispatched scores of the Persian vessels to their doom.

Such was the exploit of Skillus of Skione and of his daughter Hydna. And on a night soon after the event, swimming across from Aphetai to Artemision, they themselves bore the tidings of what had occurred.

"Fancy, eighty stades this girl swam!"

"Do you mean to say they had no boat?"

"What's that? Did you say a boat? Ask Lyko-medes, son of Aeschreas, if he is anywhere about. He was the trierarch of the ship to which the girl swam. He threw her a rope and she swarmed up it quicker than you would have done."

"Moreover, they did not come empty-handed. It was only through them our leaders got to know anything definite about the movements of the Persian fleet."

It was wonderful to have such a girl there and be in a camp so full of great happenings!

By a strange coincidence, at close quarters to each other, stood the tents of the Athenians, the Spartans, the Tegeates, the Corinthians, the Potidaians, the Sikyonians, the Epidaurians, the Troezenians; only the chapels of Androkrates and the fountains of Gargaphia were wanting to convert these low hills surrounded by the plain into a likeness of the battlefield of Plataeae. Former war comrades greeted each other, pleasantly surprised, as do people who have gone through critical times together. Memories of the past hummed around them. Somebody had saved another's life, someone had carried somebody else off the scene of action, the wounded showed each other their healed scars. Their sighs ascended for the souls of the dead. And when they lacked words they would exclaim: By Zeus! By Pallas! By Hermes! By Aias! The whole of Olympia joined in their joyful outbursts.

Larger groups mustered and, linking arms, they shouted: Salamis! or Plataeae! or Mykale! to summon those in the more remote parts of the encampment. Later they moved off towards Harpina, where there was an empty space, and sat scattered about in wide circles.

They were most eager to know what their various memories held of these experiences of the past. No records, no chronicles preserved past events, and these still took their course on the wings of rumour.

Far away, on the Karian coast, a lad of twelve years was amusing himself with cockle-shells or chasing after a little barrow drawn by a dog. Some time had still to elapse before he would start on his journey across the world, before he would hear these accounts from human lips, and before he would record them once and for all time in the work which should begin thus: "What Herodotos of Halikarnassos has heard he has set down here to the end that what has been accomplished may not be lost, more especially that the great and wonderful deeds of both the Hellenes and the Barbarians may not pass away unfamed."

Five Olympiads later the whole nation was to hear him. Here in the shade of the Sacred Circle would first echo the sweet sound of the Ionian speech from the unrolled papyrus. Time was to trace its course backwards and the passage of all those years was to be embraced in a few hours by words that would review the period from end to end. The younger generation, who on the day of the Marathon had slept with their puny fists uplifted and who after Salamis had sung a pæan in their childish voices, and those, still younger, who on the knees of their grandfathers had drowsed over these names, would at last have a full realisation of all that had hitherto lived dispersed in gossip and legend. But the greybeards, listening, hands to ears, would be puzzled at not being able to remember this man, who, notwithstanding, was to talk as if he had once been amongst them, though he had not even a single white hair to prove his presence in those times.

Whatever private opinions might be formed about

those events, they would have to give way, for who thereafter could equal in fleeting words this art of expression, so tunefully harmonious? There would then be no more contention as to whether Ephialtes or Onatas had betrayed to the Persians the passage to Thermopylae, and henceforth no occasion to hurl one's own name into the strife for the glory of having slain Mardonios. This would then be all decided and sealed. It would be futile to tap the ground with a stick, to tug at another's sleeve; you could not out-shout history with your ancient's voice.

Of course, nobody had any thought that such things were to come. For these peoples, scattered about the monuments of those who had revered the deities, there had existed through the centuries only one book, the book of recollection and tradition, intricate, unstable and infinite as the convolutions of the human brain, yet weathering all calamities, fire and devastation.

Its newest pages were being produced. They were already full of erasures, insertions and additions. Each one still entertained a measure of hope that, God willing, he would be appended as a footnote to the margin of some page. One might gain the attention of as many listeners as possible by sheer power of voice, by an apt word, by an exact description of circumstances; one would have to enter their recollections forcibly and shape these so as to leave a gap sufficient for one's own person. This would not be easy, since all had come with the same intention; indeed, the very first words gave rise to a clamour. Perhaps the best policy would be to await the opportune moment quietly, like a hulking fellow who, with his hands on his parted thighs, smiled and excited people's curiosity by his unambitious silence. Nobody remembered him.

His name was Ameinokles—Ameinokles, the son of Kretines. He came from Korope, on the Pagasaean gulf. There he had a house, a boat, a few slaves and nets. No great possessions these; but, as there was never a shortage of fish, an existence of some sort was eked out—until the rumour spread that the Great King was advancing towards Hellas. This was hard to discredit, considering that the splash of the oars could be heard. The royal ships, it is true, berthed at the farther shore of Magnesia, but Magnesia is so narrow that what occurs on that shore is heard across on this. The fleet made land between the town of Kastanai and the promontory of Sepias. A part was moored to the shore, while the rest of the fleet cast anchor, and thus the night was spent in absolute calm and quiet.

The next day, however, the sea became rough. A strong and angry wind arose, from the Hellespont. This storm, as is well known to all, was roused by Boreas in response to the prayer of the Athenians—Boreas, who was knit by wedlock to their former princess royal. Such ships as were too far from the shore the sea washed away and cast, some on Iperi near to Pelion, some on Cape Sepias, while others went aground near Kastanai or Meliboea. It was then that Skillus and his daughter loosed the anchors of a number of these ships. Ameinokles witnessed the storm, when it broke and when it passed away after raging for three days. It was rumoured that four hundred of the king's ships were shattered into splinters. And then, when the sea had quietened down, the surviving remnant of the fleet steered its course along the shores of

Magnesia. It entered the gulf and came to a stop near
Aphetai, whence, centuries ago, Jason had set out on the
quest of the Golden Fleece. Thereafter along the whole
shore many bodies of Persians were to be seen. It was
hateful finding them.

Ameinokles crossed over to the other side where there
was not a soul. The kindly gentle waves visited the shore
and brought from time to time planks, spars, oars, the
wreckage of ships. If it had not been for the corpses
which, swollen, slimy and livid, lay rotting in the summer
sun, he might have said that no dwelling was to be compared with the ship's cabin shattered and stuck between
two rocks on the lonely shore, in the infinite peace of sea
and sky. There he remained right through the war and
did not complain that it was time wasted. The waves constantly added to his possessions. There was much to do
every day, even if it were only to overturn these heaps of
sodden timber and rusting iron, beneath which articles
of some value might be discovered. As it happened, such
things were found, even more than he had expected.
There were vessels of silver and gold, caskets of money,
amulets, various implements often difficult to identify,
but always adorned with something that glittered.

He did not give any figure, but nobody expected that;
they might picture measures of gold as large as would fit
into each one's imagination. They indulged themselves
in these surmises with delight, and the ring of the bars of
gold, resounding in their brains, drowned his last words.
It was seen that Ameinokles still moved his lips, that with
his hands he gesticulated despondently, that something
akin to tears glistened in his eyes, but it was only those
sitting nearest him who could make out that what he

146

said referred to children, most probably his own, who had died one after the other. Nobody condoled with him in his grief, for he had filled them too much with his good fortune.

They were, on the other hand, only too ready to have a share in it. The soldiers, whose helmets had marked their foreheads with an indelible white streak, laid aside their initial resentment that this clown should for so long have taken up attention which would otherwise have been directed to their affairs. They were under the sway of a mercenary tendency each of them possessed, and the cockles of their hearts warmed at the thought of the riches that the conquest had provided.

They revelled in the recollection of the Persian wealth. Again, pictured by their words, the booty accumulated—the tents worked with gold and silver, the ivory-encrusted beds, goblets, bowls, sets of tableware and valuable weapons. Once again a thrill of pleasurable surprise ran down their spines, the same thrill as when in the carts, those common camp carts, they had discovered bags stuffed with kettles, basins and platters of heavy silver. They had of course stripped the corpses of their costly sabres, daggers, shoulder-badges, chains, brooches or rings. In everybody's memory there was clearly defined that huge pile, variegated and lustrous of colour, round which the scribes and accountants had busied themselves with the inventory. The Laconian helots dealt with each object separately. They presented it for registration and then bore it away to its allotted storage-place.

The distribution of the spoils had been carried out with all fairness; of prisoners, women, gold, silver and

cattle, each one had received what was his due, but it
was significant that the helots had been left too long
without supervision. Nobody said any more, because of
the Aeginetans, who sat in a group together. It was
known that they had made a good haul on that occasion; not for nothing were they descended from ants.
They found some means to deprive the helots of their
fear and distrust and bewitched them into parting with
innumerable articles of silver and gold. These they
would sell off with dispatch, for money is always easier
to secrete and to transport, but in the hurried bargaining gold was disposed of at the price of copper.

Ægina, that small island, one can imagine how such
a tiny purse filled up to overflowing! There followed a
moment of silence which the Aeginetans endured without turning a hair. Glances were focused on them. The
merchants from Miletos, from Byzantium, from Corinth
stroked their beards, silently musing the while on that
wealth which, they thought, should in no case get past
their ports. The people from Sicily and Great Greece
did not evince any interest; to them Greece as a whole
appeared like a mob of hungry ragged men, quarrelling
over chewed bones. The Athenians, on the other hand,
reflected that that rocky triangle in the Saronic gulf lies
but a step removed from their shores and that the time
was fully ripe for taking that step. Trade negotiations,
alliances, wars showed in their eyes.

A moment later the talk had drifted into another
channel. Discussion centred on how much the Persians
had managed to save. Xerxes sailed away first, and what
he took with him was altogether impossible to reckon
in terms of Greek finance. Various amounts were sug-

gested, which, running in a circle, acquired huge proportions. Above them hung a ponderous vision of riches
under which they all drooped crumbling in their own
poverty. They saw Artabazos's army fleeing northwards,
they saw the royal fleet sailing away to the east; two
horizons collided like doors violently slammed, there
was scarcely time enough to save one's fingers from being
crushed. They experienced a helpless despair, as if someone had cheated them, robbed and ransacked them.

In the void which suddenly possessed them, they felt
the oncome of that chill so familiar to their minds and
assuredly never to be forgotten. It had borne down on
them with the first news of Xerxes's expedition, as if Fate
had fluttered her wide wings. Greece seemed to be then
what she actually was, a small cramped cell on which
the fabric of the world had tumbled. For they were convinced that they were fighting against the whole world.
In the army of the great king there were soldiers drawn
from the remotest lands of the earth—Ethiopians and
Indians. How many of them were there? No reckoning
now could say. They added and multiplied unceasingly.
From time to time some other kind of weapons would be
remembered, and after every such recollection several
thousands or scores of thousands would have to be added
to the total. When they had arrived at three millions
they were too short of breath for further speculation.
Then someone would dash up explaining that this figure
ought to be doubled and he would impress them with
the vast number of ships that had carried the corn, the
livestock, the tools and gear. But before long it was
found that the serfs, the camp-followers, the cooks, the
women and the eunuchs had been left out of account

while calculating the army. Their overloaded imaginations called a halt, weighed down by this swarming ant-heap of humans.

"Imagine," said one of the Corinthians, a corn merchant, "if each one received only a choinix of wheat, I say only a choinix, then every day there were needed eleven times ten thousand three hundred and forty medimnoi. And I am not counting the women, the eunuchs, the cattle and dogs."

In their minds stretched a vista of the long rows of lofty storehouses that would be needed to hold but one day's rations, and cornfields spread out searching in vain for space amidst the mountains and rocks of Greece. There crept towards them a monstrous shape, mottled and multicoloured, clad in coats of mail, helmets and shields that might have been taken for scales, and bearing lances that bristled like sharp quills—a dragon, a new Typhon, menacing the gods and men of Hellas. But soon this solid mass began to fray, it gradually lost its strange cohesion, it shredded off ever smaller and smaller particles, until finally one faced a dozen men or so a sword's length away. Beneath the strange attire, within the folds of the long coats and in the broad embroidered trousers, were bodies flabby and weak, into which the iron entered as into dough. In the clenched fingers that had held the hilt of the sword, each one retained the memory of these easy thoughts, and the sword-point, cluttered with the souls of the slain, seemed like a purple flower under a swarm of bees.

"I'll tell you something which not everyone knows," said Lampon of Ægina suddenly. "Xerxes, when fleeing, left Mardonios all his kitchen equipment. When

we conquered the camp, Pausanias saw these articles of
gold and silver and the carpets. He ordered the royal
bakers and cooks to serve dinner, as though it were for
Mardonios. You can imagine how they prepared everything as only they could, in the very best style. It was a
sight worth seeing, those tables whereon the things of
lowest value were the goblets of crystal; and, as for the
dishes, there were so many that for half of them there
are no names in our language. Pausanias was rather
taken aback and promptly cried: 'Serve me here our
Spartan dinner.' Bringing his two earthen plates, they
placed these in the centre of all this grandeur. Pausanias
laughed heartily and said to us: 'Look, men of Hellas,
behold the stupidity of the Persians who, having such
food, ventured on a long ill-fated journey, to snatch
our coarse bread and our plate of plain broth!'"

They laughed out, but someone had already exclaimed:

"Perhaps you might tell us your other conversation
with Pausanias?"

Lampon paled and then flushed, the sweat beading
his forehead. He chafed in the midst of those hundreds
of eyes, got up and walked off without a word.

"What has come over him?"

"Don't you know? I was present at Plataeae. Running up to the Spartan king, our Lampon said: 'Son of
Kleombrotos, you have accomplished a supernatural
thing. God has empowered you to save Hellas and to
acquire renown such as nobody has had till now. Finish
the work, that your fame may be greater still, so that
in future no stranger may dare to wrong the Hellenes.
As Mardonios and Xerxes beheaded Leonidas and nailed

him to the cross in Thermopylae, they should be paid back in like manner, and so, if you crucify Mardonios, you will have wreaked vengeance for your Uncle Leonidas.' And to this Pausanias replied: 'Friend from Aegina, I appreciate your loyalty and discretion, but here you are on the wrong path. For when you exalt me, my fatherland and my feats, why do you at the same time humiliate me? And you are hurling me into the dust if you counsel that I should abuse a corpse, and, what is more, you tell me that thereby my fame will be enhanced! That may be seemly for Barbarians but not for Hellenes, and even when the Barbarians do such a thing, we consider it shameful. Leonidas deserves to be avenged, it is true, but he has already had his revenge. He has been honoured by the countless souls of those who have fallen here and those who perished in Thermopylae. So never come near me again with such advice and be happy that I let you go unpunished.' Now you know who Lampon is!"

All except the Spartans gave way to excited chatter. Several spoke at once. The groups became more and more crowded. People joined them who had no concern there. But in a great uproar it is pleasant to have a person with a ready ear at one's side. The stranger would sit and listen and with eyes aglow he would smile and say: Yes, yes, thus was it, brother! Somebody else, however, would soon break in, talking very noisily, and when several pairs of eyes started looking him over with an increasing interest, he would lapse into silence.

The immortal gods alone know what this muteness means to man, when the voice sticks in the throat, when the half-articulated word lies like a stone in the windpipe;

and on the palms, those palms that stop midway in a gesture, is borne the burden of the speaker's whole town or even his entire country mercilessly laid bare. For immediately everybody understands. Each country, each community, each village that had not joined in the great defence of the nation, not to mention also those who had fought on the side of the Persians, had long ago been noted and condemned.

If, however, one was to sit quietly, one could have peace, for here nobody treats people discourteously. It was only the Phokians who wished that, Providence willing, they might meet even a single native of Thessaly, be he the shabbiest creature, a cripple, a hunchback or the most miserable Thessalian specimen on earth, so that at last they might for once spit in his eye before the whole world.

Thessaly's treachery was common knowledge. Guided by her princes, she had submitted to the Great King, had joined with him against Greece, had burnt down and devastated whole-countries. Phokis had been trodden underfoot by her. To deny this was out of the question, but the Phokians laid an unnecessary insistence on it. Between them and Thessaly there was a perpetual hatred. They were always in opposite camps. Had Thessaly taken sides against the king, they would have been with the king and would have fired Thessalian towns. Of that there is no doubt. It had to be admitted, however, that things happened otherwise, that the Phokians fought bravely and that they endured immense losses, whereas Thessaly was a nest of traitors. With her only Thebes could be compared. That is why there were none from either place in Olympia that day. The Thebans mattered little, but for the choice Thessalian horses it was a pity.

With that thought the entire war sank into oblivion and everybody drifted towards the hippodrome, where the stables were. Some of these were still being hastily erected with whatever logs and planks came to hand. On account of the heat the horses were kept screened. Slaves stood before the linen curtains which covered the entrances. Around them moved crowds of people who addressed them and passed on before they received an answer. At times somebody would succeed in drawing the curtain a trifle, eyes would then strain through the dusky chink, from which would issue noises and the sharp odour of animals. It was said that this year there would be a great number of Persian horses, wonderfully perfect. This surmise was confirmed by the presence of many Persian grooms amongst the stable servants. Everybody knew quite well their cloth caps, their variously coloured sleeved jackets and their baggy trousers. There emanated from them the disagreeable smell of human skin encased in tight thick clothes.

These were prisoners of war apportioned after the victory. They blenched as often as someone approached them, and seemed to come to life again as if on account of repeated astonishment that no one did them any harm. They gazed at the passers-by with the submissiveness of a dog, as though it was to them that their noses, eyes, ears and limbs belonged, being no more their own.

The closed stables could not hold anyone's attention for long. The crowd gradually dispersed and merged into the humming bustle of the market quarter.

CHAPTER III

A N unlimited number of booths, shops and stalls stretched out along the roads leading into Olympia and at the boundaries of the encampment extending up to Harpina. The Agoranomoi, the officials of the mart, settled disputes about weights and measures and supervised the commerce in general. Every branch of trade had its particular site. Everything that was used for food was kept together.

The most abundantly stocked was the fish section. Spacious tubs swarmed with fat fleshy forms full of life. From within these tubs there drifted the odour of a thick scum which had been formed gradually by the dust and the sun's action on the water. But the fish that fared the worst were those which were the objects of the deal while a bargain was being driven; they paid dearly for the inflexibility of customers' money bags. They lay on the boards of the stall with their eyeballs bulging out and their tails flapping, they heaved up their fins in vain, unrefreshed by even a single drop of moisture in the dry and scorching atmosphere. At times they returned to the tubs, but oftener the knife cut through their throats. At this the butcher, isolated amid this fish traffic, looked on gloomily. Half naked, in an apron besmeared with blood, he drove off with a twig the large black flies, the only visitors to his shambles. In the penetrating heat it was difficult to lure anyone with the sight of meat and, judging from the livid spots on it, one might reasonably surmise that it would soon become offal for the dogs, which, tethered under the cart, were howling with hunger and thirst.

The corn section was quiet also. Wheat and barley flour, variously ground, were on sale; there was even a mill turned by an ass, and a handmill from which flour poured out for all to see. Under tents, surrounded by bags of grain, sat the merchants from Olbia. Important transactions were arranged here: deliveries for towns that had suffered a dearth, trade negotiations and agreements between firms and factories; lastly, landowners came here to discuss means of improving their soil. The Olbians were listened to with the respect which wealth and experience bring. Living on the islets of the Dnieper, they hailed from the neighbourhood of limitless spaces with a rich black soil, on the borders of farthest myth. They told how Achilles dwelt in their country, whom the sea-goddesses had borne there after his death. The long sandy tongue of the mainland jutting into the sea served him as a running-ground and often the darting shadow of the hero was seen, like a fleeting white haze. They told this on the strength of sailors' reports, as if the mere sight of such nimbleness were too great an effort for their obese, unwieldy selves.

Behind their tents, tables laden with the fresh pastry gave out a warm aroma. Everybody had had enough of the mazai, hard flat cakes which were broken into small pieces and taken together with pure wine for early breakfast. But more than one mountaineer or peasant newly come from the barren areas saw for the first time real wheaten bread with a dark crust and a startlingly white crumb. Others picked and chose at great length among the rolls, surprised at their diverse shapes: for they were like star-shells, crescents, and all kinds of animals, feminine breasts and the genitalia. Cakes with cheese, with poppy-seeds, with sesame-seeds, honey-baked, were brought, still hot, on wide boards.

The fruit-stalls were enriched by the blushes of apples, by the gold of pears, by the fragrance of dates. When purchasing nuts a few leaves were asked for; these, stuffed into the parcel, kept away vermin. Above the green bundles of cress and chervil, the head of lettuce, the bunches of garlic and onion, immense Sikyonian cucumbers stood out prominently. The people who bought these ran the gauntlet of the Cyprian who sold spices at the booth alongside. At heavy cost he had acquired from somewhere a bag of pepper and in stentorian tones he was proclaiming its good qualities. He spoke of the Indies which are at the earth's extremity, of turbulent seas and of flying serpents; the tiny black grains which he held in his palm were the fruit of fearful adventures; a host of people had to pay for them with their lives, and yet he was prepared to give one cyathus-full for two obols. Nobody could afford such extravagance. But the Cyprian's flowing tongue robbed the dishes of all their relish; it scoffed at the distrust of the people who, he presumed, had never peeped beyond the smoke of their own hovels. When he shaded his eyes with his palm, looking out for "his regular customers, the gentlemen from Sicily", to see if they were arriving, someone might succeed in driving a bargain with him for half an obol.

The eating-houses advertised themselves from afar by the pervading fumes of olive-oil. Under a linen awning stood the kitchens with masonry foundations and fire-places over which tripods of iron supported large kettles and frying-pans. It could be seen how a fish freshly cleaned and scaled was put into the pan, how olive-oil and wine were poured over it, how it was seasoned with spices and finally tossed on to a plate, how it was sprinkled with a pinch of silphion, which gives an inviting flavour.

The people ate standing, with a spoon or with their fingers, under their arms a piece of bread from which they took a bite now and again. The plate was returned to the proprietor licked clean; the grease sticking round the lips and chin was wiped away with a crumb of bread and this moist sticky lump was thrown to the hens clucking in the coops.

Nobody now denied himself a goblet of wine. The wine-bars were lodged in arbours propped up by a few posts, with a roof made of twigs and leaves. Beside each of them a pit was dug into the earth to provide a cover for the earthen jars, and keep them cool. Of the wines there were three varieties: the dark sort, which was deep red, like the blood in the arteries; the white kind, which was pale like straw; and the yellow variety of a golden hue. The last-mentioned was the best for digestion; it had just the right properties, for the black variety was too thick and strong, the white, on the other hand, too thin and weak. Naturally everybody had his own particular favourites, and connoisseurs would hesitate for a long while, like ships gone astray, between Phlius, Sikyon, Chios, Lesbos, Thasos, Rhodes and Knidos. In any case, no one drank the wine neat. It was diluted to two-thirds or even three-fifths with water. Boys, out of breath, ran with hydrias to the wells some stades away. Some were contented with water alone and lifted the cool pitcher to their lips with delight. Elsewhere myrinites was carried around: wine spiced with the juice of the myrtle-berry, having an intoxicating odour. Pedlars with jugs of cider, fig-wine and date-wine, also loitered about. But it was only on the outskirts of this settlement of tastes that the crowd was thickest.

An extensive colony of shops, which increased in number day by day, stocked everything except weapons. These were not only unprocurable from the merchants but possessed by nobody in the whole encampment. The pilgrims from afar, whose way led through mountains and lonely deserts where the truce of the gods could hardly be relied upon, arrived armed, but they left all their weapons at the frontier of Elis. There, in special stores, their swords, bows, spears and slings were kept till they should call for them on their return. With this exception everything was to be found here that could be of use to people hundreds and thousands of stades away from their homes.

Tools, nails, wheels for carriages, vessels, utensils, gathered in an enormous quantity, appeared, so it seemed, to be a common market-pile reserved for make-shifts in urgent and unforeseen contingencies. However, it was seldom that the proper advantage was taken of these things, seldom did someone press through the crowd, buy a tub or a comb and return with it to make up the deficiency in the equipment of his shelter. For actually nobody was in want of anything. Each one had started provisioned for the few months of travel, and in his luggage a few superfluous things would be found, rather than a lack of necessary articles. In spite of this, everybody would pick things out, bicker about the price and, loaded with different objects, prowl about continually searching.

The vessels from the Athenian potteries, with their quaint shapes and the attraction of the curious scenes that were painted on them, were a ready bait. The chairs, tables and stools of Miletos had nothing to equal them for comfort, for the excellence of their wood and their artistic production. Ropes were in demand at the ropemakers' who came from the environs of Marathon. The Corinthian merchants clanged spoons against large porringers that the admirable sound of their bronze might be heard. The jewellers, behind wooden grilles amidst their rainbow-coloured treasures, exhibited the mystery of the amber which, after it had been rubbed with cloth, caught up hairs and fibres. Around the shops selling olive-oils and salves were diffused various aromas, many of which had absolutely no names of their own and came like a whisper from a strange land. On the Oriental carpets griffins and winged bulls guarded the tree of life, and the Phoenician purple gave the dark hue of the sea, covered by a violet haze.

Queer animals had been brought over from the colonies. There were lions, panthers, ostriches which would hide their tiny heads in the coats of the passers-by, and apes that occasioned excited laughter because of their similarity to man. A Megarian, who had received a camel as his share of the Persian spoils, took boys riding and charged half an obol for three rides. On a high perch stood perturbed screeching peacocks and next to them was a long platform of planks on which slaves were being auctioned. For the most part they were naked; the men's muscles were being examined, the girls' and women's breasts and hips; some of them sat at looms or made embroideries to show their skill. Only the prisoners of war were allowed their wearing apparel, the Caspians their furs, the Chalybes their red puttees; the Sicilians brought with them a couple of dozen or so Carthaginians whom they had captured at Himera. Notwithstanding their exorbitant prices they were purchased in the hope that these fellow-countrymen of Kadmos would display a knowledge of the rare handicrafts, arts and magic. A few Ethiopian striplings with plaited hair heaped up in high coiffures, with bodies moulded seemingly out of bronze, would leer at the crowd from which somebody's hands might reach out in longing for their youth and shapeliness.

People who all their lives had wanted nothing more than their chiton or their chlamys, woven and cut by their mothers, their wives or their slave girls, experienced a strange sensation on seeing the linen and wools in all colours—chiefly white, yellow, red and green—and the ready-made clothes of patterned designs. There were cloaks with stars, flowers, with designs of animals, representations of war-scenes, of hunts, of myths. The Byzantine unfolded a magnificent garment with a green border on which were embroidered ducks in gold. Before one could recover from one's astonishment, out from the crowd came a rustic dressed in a dipthera (a thick leather cloak), who extracted from his mouth, from somewhere under the gums, a silver coin, paid it up without bargaining and, slinging the robe over his shoulder, departed expressionless amid the jests of the bystanders, overcome as he was by a piercing realisation of his folly.

Each one had a mind to carry away some oddment from this bewildering diversity of the outer world. The most insignificant object became a souvenir, novel in its shape or in the way it was wrought. There were not to be found two articles exactly alike. On each thing special thought, care and patience had been expended. Together with the idea, the artisan had imparted to his works the tradition, the custom, the temperament, the breath of his environment. Once purchased, they travelled a long way through space and time to abide among strange people like a handful of coagulated words, a pithy and convincing statement about horizons that do not end at the outskirts of the native village. Forms, lines, motifs clung, creeper-like, to the new soil, developed or were transformed by hands inspired by their foreign qualities; they travelled along the routes of caravans and expeditions, to interweave unexpectedly with the very spirit of countries and nations existing beyond the limits of conjecture, in the fjords of Scandinavia, on the Slav lowlands, amidst the wastes of Tibet.

Those of lesser means, having cast off the inactivity which the abounding rich shops had imposed on them, thronged round the trifles of no price at all: several of these they bought together, so as in the end to make up the value of half or a quarter of an obol. There were pipes, baskets, children's toy carts, wax or clay dolls with movable limbs, ribbons, earrings, bronze and copper bracelets, earthen lamps for olive-oil, an inexhaustible mound of brittle and fragile articles for which the return journey would be sure to set many snares. The greatest possible number of them would have to be taken in order that those tiny hands which would stretch out for them might not be left empty and that, above all, something too should be found in that palm which had for so long been shading the eyes, looking through the sunlight and dust for the husband's cart.

The embassies and pilgrims, especially those from places not far distant, had brought along their own animals for the offerings, but a goodly number did not buy them until they reached Olympia. The oxen, heifers, and sheep, in large herds, were kept in enclosures and stands along the Alpheios. Over each animal the haggling dragged on for so long that it seemed agreement would never be reached. The beast was examined from the edges of its cloven hoofs to the tip of its horns; the buyer handled every part of the body as if he would feel through the hide to know if the entrails functioned normally; each little speck on its immaculate whiteness would alarm him so much that it seemed he was counting every hair. He would be plunged into a painful anxiety that the animal might reveal some defect, some symptom that would cause it ultimately to be driven away from the altar. Barley would be scattered before the bulls and, if they did not eat enough, they were considered to be ill. People would shout, rail, bargain and turn away; they would call all their relatives and acquaintances for a conference; would come back, fearing that prices might rise during the last days.

Those who could not afford to pay five drachmas for a bull, nor three for a heifer, nor one for a sheep, stood at the extreme edge of this hubbub, silent and envious.

For them the neighbouring booths exhibited poor semblances of offerings: animals moulded in wax or dough, earthen or bronze votive offerings, flowers and incense. But here, too, the wealthy had been considered. On special stalls small vessels with water collected from the miraculous wells, bunches of greenery culled from the graves of demi-gods and heroes or grown on some sacred post, thunderbolts, and fragments of meteorites were to be seen. Amulets of gold, silver, copper, of burnt clay, or of stone represented various sacred symbols, phallic or female, disgusting forms of Oriental demons, or magic words in an unknown script. A Thracian peasant, an immense moustached burly fellow in trousers, folded small pats of yellow rancid butter into leaves, purchased as healing ointment.

At various places in the marketing-quarter sat the money-changers. Their hands in an unceasing movement seemed to be spinning the web of silver which encompassed the entire encampment as in an intangible net. Before them lay piles of coins, arranged according to their shape and value; there were spread out thin spangles, the half and quarter obols; in an unordered mass were heaped coins worn, covered with verdigris and blackened by acids and moisture. Every now and then somebody would consent to exchange money of his own country into whatever currency the foreign merchant had demanded of him, or would change a bigger piece for smaller ones. Old plain-backed coins were produced, bearing an emblem on one face, and new ones with an effigy of a deity on one side and a sacred symbol on the other. The coins of Ægina were to be recognised by the tortoise, the animal of the Heavenly Aphrodite;

Croton had the Apollonine tripod, Lydia the lion of the Great Mother of the Gods. Pegasus spread his wings on the Corinthian staters, the monstrous form of the Minotaur, crouching, encircled the Cretan didrachma, Europa rode on the bull, Heracles was shown resting in the garden of the Hesperides. On others there were neither deities nor sacred symbols, but in a succulent stalk of the Kyrenian silphion the actual wealth of that country was represented, while in the case of the Metapontine coins there ripened a wonderful wheat-ear with a grasshopper swinging on its awns.

The money-changers alone had a knowledge of the weight and value of all Greek towns and colonies and the Barbarian countries. They would allay the doubts that divorced these little silver discs, eternally clashing with each other their fractional differences in weight and metal. Only from them did the Spartans get considera-tion for their iron money, but they were embittered at receiving a few silver spangles for their heavy bags jingling with the worthless stuff. The coins from Kos and from Aspendos, however, that bore the figure of the discus-thrower, circulated above their nominal value, for many contestants would take them as lucky charms. Disputes arose over the currencies that had no equivalent value. These would be put on the scales and the metal would be tested on a touchstone, although the eye of the money-changer had differentiated from a distance the "white gold" or electron from pure silver and had noticed the edge of the coin where the scissors had passed, cut-ting off from it a strip a hair's breadth in thickness. Seldom did one have recourse to the intervention of the agoranomoi in these altercations. They were settled by the money-changers themselves, with that particular dry gesture peculiar to them only, and the coin, pushed away to the edge of the table, would appear as if hurled beyond the world's end. It was known that the same fate would be met with at all the other tables; more than one would conceive a superstitious fear that his base coin had been marked down in the tablet of wax, clay or wood, or on the papyri, covered with calculations, which were held in the hands of the money-changers. In reality, these writings were records of debts, of draft warrants, of pawnings, the first transactions of this kind which, like pre-arranged flash signals, appeared here and there in some of the trading towns, strange and tempting fore-runners of money traffic.

The Olympian mart bore no comparison to any other. The markets of the great towns such as Byzantium, Miletos, Syracuse, Akragas, would appear minute and dull beside it. They lacked that particular universality; each existed, narrowed by restrictions, customs duties, mortgages, by anxiety and avarice, through schemes that were hampered by the situation and the nature of the soil. Here, however, there had developed a town apparently rid of all earthly defects, where every day was a holiday, where all thoughts referred to pleasant and blissful things—a town that had sprung up on the threshold of the spirit, as it were, on the very brink of Utopia. So compendious was its brief and charming existence that its acquaintance was barely made when it would lapse into a memory. One entered into it at ease and the next morning one already moved about it with the composure and carelessness of long-standing habit; newcomers with their excited ways, like country people, were viewed with a smile; the day abounded in innumerable trifles which devoured it unnoticed.

The barbers' shops opened at daybreak, as do those in the market of a large town. In the front of each there would be placed some chairs which were never unoccupied. Long hair was twisted into plaits, and these were either allowed to hang down the back or were rolled into thick bundles and held together with pins or tied with ribbons; the locks over the forehead and temples were singed and then made up like stars or rosettes in the form of a wreath. Some kept their moustaches, while others had them shaved off with a sharp sickle-like curved razor which, causing much pain, would scrape away the hair that had scarcely been softened with the warm olive-oil. The beards were trimmed into a wedge-shape, some having them curled in long wavy strands. But the young men would get rid of the luxuriant locks, they would have themselves cropped short like the wrestlers and boxers and many would submit their first down to the razor. The old people looked on at them without being shocked; nobody was inclined to question the new times which bared the bright countenance of an ephebe.

In the traffic around the barbers' shop there swarmed frequent customers and gossip-mongers. All news and rumours were carried there, happenings at the extremities of the world were talked about, events that were most recent and yet as distant as the ray of an extinct star. Gossip was shrouded with an international glamour, in it there was that singular relish with which one enjoyed the secrets of Africa, Asia and Europe as if they were those of the next-door neighbours. The mountaineers of

Arcadia or Epeiros, at all times to be found standing behind someone's back, as though unable to forsake their native heights which limited their outlook, allowed the moments of appropriate silence to pass by, feeling that this was not the time for silly stories about a mare which gave birth to a hare or about doubled-headed calves. Sometimes beggars would appear—those untouchable vagabonds, patronised by Zeus, who were everywhere, their laments and outcries stripping off some shred of their life whereon would be the trace of blood or the dust of immeasurable roads. Mariners, with bright eyes bathed as it were by space, would suddenly emerge from their silence with a tale about foaming water, golden mountains, volcanic islands, about a country of Blessedness lying on the great continent behind the Ocean, and everybody with bated breath and a strained gaze hung upon the lips of the speakers, as if in expectation that ultimately some word would carry them beyond this clump of earth which was at the moment their entire world.

CHAPTER IV

THE GROVE OF ZEUS

O<small>N</small> the tenth day of the month Parthenios the competitors set out from Elis. They were about three hundred. Since the last full moon much change had taken place, new people had arrived; Drakon of Argos, the champion in a previous Olympiad, was among the youths; Theognetos, who came behind him, took the shortest steps possible in order to avoid treading on him. For the long journey on foot they wore only chitons or chlamydes, which they flung over their bare bodies. Some had got so much out of the habit of wearing clothing of any sort that they found even this light apparel a burden and an impediment. The rest of the baggage they deposited on the carts following in rear.

Behind these trotted a batch of horses that had arrived at the last moment. On their heads they had linen cowls as sun-guards and their hooves were shielded by clumsy leather bags shaped like boots. The animals, impatient at the tardy pace, tugged at their bridles. Ultimately they were given rein to move onwards and the accompanying grooms rode them.

The last ranks of the competitors now were followed by the princes' conveyances. Under purple hoods sat Hieron of Syracuse, accompanied by his brother-in-law Chromios, who was returning from Nemea with a recently acquired championship; Theron of Akragas with his son Thrasidaios, the ruler of Himera, and Arkesilas from Cyrene. These sent their horses to every Olympiad. Their splendour was swelled by the various descendants of the gods from Argolis, Boeotia, Attica and Euboea. Traditionally, through the ages, all aristocracies kept horses.

Driving separately was the Macedonian king, Alexander, the son of Amyntas, in a Persian chariot overlaid with gold glittering with representations of the sun, moon and stars. Twenty years ago he himself had competed in the races on the stadium. At first they did not want to admit him, as he was considered not to be of pure Grecian blood. But he had referred to his descent from the kings of Argos, he had pieced together a fictitious genealogy in the hope that by means of a championship he might inscribe himself for all time in the golden book of Panhellenic nobility. The wreath had eluded him, but still through his services in the Persian wars he had merited esteem and friendship. His conduct at Plataeae was remembered and now everybody greeted him.

Next followed the carriages of the hellanodikai, those of members of the Council or of the priests. Farther to the rear came the sacrificial animals, scores of oxen, cows and sheep, the hecatomb of the Eleians, and in the midst of their spotless white could be seen the fat black ram destined for the grave of Pelops. A special cart carried the iron cage containing the wild boar that had been trapped in the Arcadian mountains. On his blood the oath of the competitors was to be taken. The rest of the column was made up by late-coming pilgrims and processions from Elis itself.

The animals and vehicles were decorated with foliage, and everybody had a wreath on his head or a flower in his hair. Suddenly from the general buzz the powerful voice of one of the priests emerged; in the ensuing silence an endeavour was made to follow the words and with the next stanza the hymn was sung by all.

The "Sacred Way" stretched along the sea, which for the first few score stades was screened by hills. But at the last they dropped away, unveiling the sandy coast to the west. A few rivulets cut across the road which, without bridges, led down along the waterless river-beds; on the pebbles the carriages resounded with a clatter. A single and only bridge spanned the one river that, between high banks, preserved a trace of water. This was the Iardanos, perpetuating in its name the memory of the Phoenicians—Iardanos which is eulogised by the few verses of Homer that tell of the combat between Nestor and the Arcadians.

The sun dipped towards the sea when the column came to a halt at the spring of Piera.

From out of the thick brushwood there trickled a threadlike rill which, a stade beyond, dried up in the sands. In this brooklet the old-time frontier between Elis and Pisa lived in memory. On the farther side lay the sacred country of Olympia. Everybody climbed down from the carts and one of the priests took from an attendant a month-old piglet which squealed piercingly. Catching it by the ears, he slit its throat with a deep cut of the knife. Some of the blood bespattered his chiton and the rest spurted into the spring, changing the colour of the darkened water like the reflection of the setting sun. All in turn immersed their hands in the brook, and

besprinkled their garments, fulfilling the ritual of purifi-
cation.

The night was spent in Letrinoi, a small town near by
which subsisted on its earnings from pilgrims. It functioned as one large inn, where everybody found a bed
and a pitcher of excellent wine.

With the dawn they moved on. About noon, from
among the ranges Dyspontion emerged, facing the
broad river Alpheios. The river flowed in the middle of
a huge bed, bending and breaking up in all directions
amid the sandbanks and islets bared by the summer
droughts. Ships coming from the estuary were still able
to reach this spot, and the roads from the south, from
Triphylia and Messenia terminated at the ford where
ferry-boats were being hailed. But the procession avoided
this clamour by keeping to the right bank. Once more
it was screened by hills and unexpectedly hove in sight
of the crowd encamped in the Olympic valley.

A mighty cheer greeted it. The hellanodikai moved
up to the head of the column in order to open a passage
through the throng with their purple. The competitors
were put into the middle of the procession to shield them
from being troubled by the surging mass. Some of them,
however, were recognised and people from their towns
called out to them by name. The horses shied and reared;
the dignitaries alighted from the carriages and the
rhabduchi helped the attendants to lead the animals
away to the stables. A party of Athenians snatched King
Alexander onto their shoulders and bore him to his
camp.

Meanwhile the competitors were ushered into the
Altis and the gates were closed behind them. Hysmon,

who remained with them, explained where they would find the barracks that had been prepared for their night-quarters. Nobody heeded him. The solemn whisper of the sacred grove, it seemed, had deafened them to all human sounds. Sotion, standing in the first row, looked around at the trees in wonder. The footpath which led on from under his feet was lost a few paces ahead in the wood. Hysmon guessed what he looked for:

"The stadium," he said, "is on yonder side. Drakon will lead you."

They walked forward in single file. The white poplars bore broad crowns on their tapering trunks, and below the silvery trembling of their leaves the olives maintained a golden silence. Birds were heard in the brush-wood. Here and there a freshly whitened altar peeped through. All of a sudden the trees parted and in the centre of a small clearing was a hillock with a few pines on its crest. A low pentagonal wall surrounded it. This was the barrow of Pelops.

Glancing at this green mound, denuded by the rains and storms of the ages, they entered the stern atmosphere of myths.

It appeared to them that they were looking at King Oinomaos, black-bearded and with a sombre glance from under drooping eyebrows as he leant upon his spear, gazing at the cloud of dust on the road; that at his side stood Hippodamia, his beautiful daughter, her fair tresses falling over her shoulders, and that she pressed her hand against her heart and quivered, listening to the ever-approaching clatter of hoofs. Again a prince is arriving to ask for her hand. He has arrived, he greets the king. His raven hair is plaited in ringlets around his tanned face;

it is Pelops. The sea has brought him from far-off Lydia. King Oinomaos says: "If you win the race, I will give my daughter; otherwise I shall slay you with this spear. Before you there have been thirteen, and all lie under the sod." The horses are harnessed, the chariots are manned, they fly on the wings of the wind. In the scorching glare of the melting distance a cry is heard. Hippodamia closes her eyes. Someone's hands are on her hair, the tanned face of the Lydian is close to hers. The attendants carry the king out from his splintered chariot.

"The races in those times must have been terrible," remarked Telesikrates. "They drove through fields and ditches. There was no hippodrome then, I suppose?"

"What hippodrome could there be?" said Ikkos. "As far as I know it was Pelops himself who arranged the first Games, at Oinomaos's funeral."

"But I heard from the Eleians," said Epharmostos, "that long before then Zeus had fought here with Kronos for the world. They fought exactly as wrestlers do. Zeus overthrew his father and pinned him down. After that he arranged Games at which Apollo outran Hermes in the racing."

"It is difficult to say anything definite about all this," interjected Sodamos. "At that time perhaps there were still no human beings even. One thing is certain, the Olympic Games were started by Heracles."

"Which one?" asked Drakon.

"And which other can there be?"

"They say here that it was the Idaean. The one who came from Crete with his brothers, the Curetes."

"That is some muddled legend. There was only one Heracles, the son of Alkmene. He it was who measured out the stadium and established the Games. He brought the poplar and the olive from the land of eternal spring, from the Hyperboreans on the Ister."

"On the Ister?" inquired Philon of Tyras, astonished. "That's not far from us. The olive does not grow there any more."

"Heracles took a graft from our Athenian olive and planted it here," said Kallias.

But Gerenos, moving a few paces away, inspected an isolated post.

"What's this?"

"This was the house of Oinomaos," answered Drakon. "Zeus struck it down with lightning."

The entire group surrounded the post, which was split in many places and dabbed over with pitch. Next to it was a stone barrier, such as is always set up at spots that have been struck by lightning. They all gazed at this bit of ground on which even grass did not grow, as if the terrible divine fire were burning here perpetually. Their glances stopped at the circle of stones, then strayed towards the two altars standing close by and returned to the blackened post. They stood spell-bound by the mystery of this site.

But in the depth of the earth, hard by the post, where sight could not reach, lay the remnants of the old-time hovels made of unshaped stone from the river and filled with a vast number of flint implements, crude pots— the traces of a vanished generation from which only a child's bones, secreted in a large earthen pitcher, have been saved. Beneath the layers of sand, earth and ashes there glimmered like a phosphorescent flame in the rotting dust the memory of times when Olympia had

no name and when Zeus had not claimed her yet with
his lightning. Undoubtedly, in these extinct settlements,
known to nobody, the roots of a creed must have existed
which flowered on the surface of the grove into many
an altar. From the generations that had passed into the
beyond there remained spirits, demons, shadows, name-
less figures of demigods, detached words, a great number
of things, possessed of an infinite power to persist and
live on, even though they were never material.

Kallias, the descendant of the Eleusinian priests, who
would one day himself be the torch-bearer, feeling as if
by a hereditary instinct the singularity of this site,
extended three fingers of his right hand in the habitual
gesture of a man sprinkling incense on an altar. But the
others had started to move; they had caught sight of the
statues that peeped out from behind the trees. Sotion
became impatient:

"Time enough for that," he said, and drew Drakon
along with him.

"Is this the spot already?" he asked, when a level wide
space opened out before them.

The youth nodded.

Having emerged from the glen, they saw now before
them a clear field bordered by the hills by the banks of
the river.

"There, to your right," said Drakon, "you see the
hippodrome. It stretches along the Alpheios up to the
ranges of Pisa. And here, where we are standing, is the
stadium. It begins at the great altar."

The great altar of Zeus was on the left, slightly to
the rear, and when they looked back at it they saw behind
it the temple and, nearer still, a terrace ascending in

steps. On it was a row of small temples and higher up, overgrown with pines, the Hill of Kronos rose in a gentle slope.

The hippodrome stood well to one side, separated by a green strip obviously made by a shrub-covered bank of earth. But the stadium had no definite shape. Broad at its base, which was formed by a line made by the last row of trees of the Grove, it narrowed towards the east, like a piece of cloth awkwardly cut. It was impossible to judge beforehand how the rectangle of the track would be outlined there.

Fresh sand had not yet been strewn over it and it was not even levelled. There were to be seen the hollows and ditches which had been scooped out by the rain streams that had coursed down during the winter from the Hill of Kronos. The competitors felt disappointed standing there, at the edge of that field marked with crowsfeet and wrinkles.

Above them shrill whistling sounds could be heard. The swallows were soaring. Their marvellous speed was exciting to watch. Everybody's eyes were glued to their wings, counting the infinitesimal moments of the flight from the start to the goal. In the end their heads weighed heavy on their craned necks; inwardly they sighed with the fatigue of the two-days' march.

They re-entered the Altis. But this was some other path, and at a certain spot Drakon whispered:

"Kallistephanos."

Here there were many olive-trees growing, but they did not know which of these is "the one that supplies the beautiful wreaths". The boy pointed out to them one, standing separate, aged, bent and shrivelled. From the trunk, split with fissures, there grew out two sinuous branches resembling swollen muscles, that, like arm outspread, presented to the sun their greyish-green offering.

So this was Kallistephanos; with this name mothers would lull their sons to sleep. So many ambitions had been pinned to it that, if its top reached to heaven and it were all of gold, it would appear less strange than this poor common-place shape. Covered with moss, swarming with ants, and strewing rotted dust from the bird-holes, it impressed one by its very hoariness; it was like Father Time himself. In one place there floated a cobweb, as when the Delphic oracle said to King Iphitos:

"Crown the victors with the wild olive, fruitful
     among its kind,
  Which now wears as a garment the fine webs
     of the spider."

A light breeze opened out the sparse crown of the tree; each twig was separately visible; they drooped without moving the tiny leaves; these could be counted, they would certainly not be sufficient for even half of those who were encompassing them at this moment with a fervent glance. Near by was the altar of the nymphs who guarded the sacred tree. After a few paces Drakon led them out to the processional way which terminated at the entrance gate. One of the rhabduchi opened the gate and, behold, there were the barracks and not far away the Bouleuterion, the premises of the Council, revealing the apses of its two wings. A noisy crowd thronged around the building.

"What's happening there?" inquired Sotion.

"I don't know," answered Drakon. "Something or

other. The epimeletes resides there, he manages the Olympian treasury."

But this time it was not the Olympian treasury the people were interested in. The crowd was stirred by the appearance of two men who, without greeting anybody, disappeared into the Bouleuterion. The old one nobody knew; the name of the younger was on everybody's lips: Theagenes of Thasos.

In the last Olympiad he had entered for the pancration and boxing. On account of the war there had not been many competitors, but in the boxing Theagenes had had a powerful opponent, Euthymos of Lokroi. In the end Theagenes had struck him on the fingers of the open left had, thereby dislocating Euthymos's wrist, and so had won. He was, however, so exhausted that he could not go on to the pancration, in which he had only one opponent, the Arcadian Dromeus from Mantinea. Dromeus was awarded the wreath, as the expression is, "without touching the sand". It was acknowledged that Theagenes was plainly responsible for this scandalous contretemps. Why had he gone in for a double event without calculating his strength in advance? He had sinned by reason of vainglory and had offended Zeus; his penalty was a fine: he had to pay one talent weight of silver to the Olympian treasury and another talent to Euthymos. The reasons for the verdict were not known; one could only suppose that the hellanodikai had wished, in this manner, to honour Euthymos, who had previously been an Olympic victor.

And now Theagenes stood before the epimeletes to pay his fine. The scales were brought. The bronze scale-pan resounded with silver in a variety of coins and in separate unstamped pieces. Together with the testing of the metal this weighing took a long time; some coins were rejected as being of no worth. Theagenes's companion, a sturdy Phoenician, would lay down fresh pieces after a little bargaining. He was a representative of the Government of Thasos, which was paying the fine for its Olympic victor. The reckoning being ended, they were asked about the money for Euthymos.

"I'll settle that with him personally," said Theagenes, and walked out.

In some inexplicable way all that was taking place in the Bouleuterion was conveyed almost simultaneously to the crowd, and through the crowd to the competitors who were standing by their barracks.

"Not an obol will he give him, I am sure," said Ikkos.

"What then?"

"He will probably offer him something worth a talent of silver."

Drakon, who did not know Ikkos, had the courage to inquire:

"What do you mean?"

"Why, what would you say if Theagenes promised you that he would not fight you any more? If Theagenes joins the boxers' list, I will allow you to call me a peastick."

But, as this information affected Menalkes especially, he inquired:

"Do you suppose that Euthymos——?"

"Yes, my handsome Opountian, you will have to reckon with him."

The crowd drifted away from the Bouleuterion, the

hillsides began to partake of the night that was already spread over the valley. The competitors entered the barracks.

In the long rectangular room two rows of beds were separated by a narrow aisle, and linen curtains took the place of doors. There was a smell of fresh wood. The stars peeped through the chinks of the roof. From the encampment at Olympia came a hum, at times there would burst out a louder cry, laughter, or a snatch of song; the competitors listened to these sounds attentively, searching for prophetic signs in them. But they died away and faded nightly into the quiet night which was made up of the river's purling sound, the croaking of frogs and the chirping of crickets. Their bodies saturated with ozone, the athletes sank into a dreamless sleep.

Next day, the twelfth, was a free day. The hellanodikai went to a Council meeting and so the competitors had no tasks. But before they were able to ponder over this leisure, the barracks were overrun by the crowd who from daybreak had been quarrelling with the rhabduchi at the Bouleuterion. There arose a commotion, a disorder, hustling and jostling, strangers leaped on the beds, names were bawled out and repeated wrongly; there was much laughter, and once someone burst out sobbing. For here ended long separations, times without news, full of anxiety; it had depended on tempests, pirates and unforeseen occurrences whether arms would now clasp in their embraces a father, a brother or a friend, who might have been kept from them for ever. An old man pushed through the crowd and called: "Mnaseas! Mnaseas!" louder and louder. As long as he had to shout the uproar down he had sufficient strength in his lungs, but when, finally, complete silence answered his cries he cast one frightened, wide-eyed glance around and, gasping for breath, collapsed senseless. He was carried away and everyone left for the camp.

There remained only Ergoteles. The old country did not claim him, and in the new one his roots were still too shallow. The house, the wife, the son in the cradle, a field bringing in a thousand medimnoi of wheat, the Carthaginian prisoners of war at the hand-mills—that was all he had in the world under a sky which none of his forbears had seen, in a distant land where none of them reposed. Man has too little significance when he has only his own shadow for company. The four syllables which are comprised in his name are common enough and yet nobody has uttered them to-day, not even by mistake.

All of a sudden he was called. Sotion stood beside him: "I have been to the camp," he said. "I went to pay my greetings to my father and then to his brother, after that to another uncle and then to yet another; then there were six uncles on my mother's side and an indefinite number of distant relatives. My arms embraced the whole of Tarentum. I ate two cakes in each tent. I poured out wine to the gods, and now a new river is flowing into the Alpheios. By Zeus! thirteen hundred and twenty-six friendly elbow-digs into bellies alone, not counting those I dealt out to thighs and backs! I beat a quick retreat. You have no idea what is going on there! Sodomos immediately quarrelled with his brother about some stools which he had not brought. Ikkos, it seems, has found his guardians, for I saw how he spat in the direction of two greybeards. Telesikrates would have me meet his father, but I managed to tear myself away. I saw his tent only from a distance. Believe me, you would need a team of four horses to get there!"

Ergoteles bent over Sotion's rapid never-ceasing flow of words as over a mountain stream. The freshness of the woods was in Sotion's breath, his laughing eyes changed colour in the speckled shade of the maple. His chlamys covered his sunburnt body like a white mist. Swift as the wind, he shook it every few minutes and raised it with his gestures. The light material would puff out like a bell and his slim nakedness shone like bronze.

"Where is Gerenos?"

"Ever since morning he has been roaming about in Olympia, as if he were searching for something he had lost in his previous existence."

"Perhaps we might go there too? I met someone here who has promised to show me round the temple."

"Which?"

"Of Hera. There is no other here."

This was the voice of the man of whom Sotion had spoken. It was uncertain whence he came, he seemed to have sprouted out of the earth suddenly and silently, like a mushroom. He was the kleiduchos, the guardian of the temple, and the dignity of his office he carried in a great iron key by a strap across his shoulders. He led them by the same path on which they had gone with Drakon the day before. The trees were laden with votive offerings, a thing they had not previously noticed.

Everywhere were hanging miniature carts, wheels, double-edged axes, swords, helmets, shields, spear-heads, tripods, diminutive cymbals, diadems, clasps, shoulder badges, rings, earrings, combs; like children's toys; here and there the tiny bronze figure of a man, fixed to a branch by the hook that grew out of his head, commemorated some victor of an epoch when as yet there were no statues; the ill-carved models of horses, with thin legs and over-large heads, told of races dimmed by time; clay figures of women holding hands danced round in a circle; a yet older human shape would rock like a bell, or a figure with legs pressed together, and arms folded across swelling breasts, with face devoid of mouth and eyes and streaked only with a long nose, and with the eternal symbol of female fecundity, represented the goddess of Love and Life. From amongst the indigenous herd, the hippopotamus, the sphinx or the Assyrian winged demon would burst forth unexpectedly like an exclamation in a foreign tongue.

These bits of bronze covered with verdigris blended in their greenness with that of the olives, poplars and plane-trees, and appeared like some strange fruit spreading up to the highest branches. Others lay on the ground, blown down by the wind, and these the kleiduchos would collect and hang up again. Their inexhaustible profusion reflected the vastness of bygone time, and the two competitors walked as if through a spectral haze, peaceful in mind, feeling that behind them they had the hosts of the dead who would assist them.

The Heraion was just behind the Pelopion. This old building stood on thick oaken posts and in their row of black the eye was struck by the bright gleam that came from a stone pillar. This had been put in to replace a decayed post. The kleiduchos explained that there were already ten such columns on the side towards the hill.

"There, to the north, greater damage is done to them by the rains."

Above the posts were placed wooden beams supporting the sloping roof with burnt clay cornices painted in red and pale blue with light yellow lines, twigs and flowers. The gutters ended in lions' heads with open jaws. A few steps took them up to the entrance-hall, and the kleiduchos inserted his iron key into the lock. The tall bronze-plated doors opened inwards and through them a strong stream of light came pouring in. It stopped a few paces away from the threshold, as if intimidated by the dusk of the lengthy interior which was divided into three naves by two rows of columns. Above them towered the roof with thick transverse rafters. The walls were made of bricks on a stone foundation, and here and there they showed greyish-yellow through the stucco-work, where it had worn away.

"The earth beneath the floor was taken from the summit of Kronion," said the kleiduchos, and he beckoned for them to come in beyond the lighted area.

Inside, away from the entrance of the temple, against the wall, on a pedestal that occupied the whole breadth of the central nave, was the statue of Zeus. The deity stood upright, leaning on a sceptre as on a spear, wearing a helmet on his head. It was Zeus Areios, the stern god of the old times, the god of the first ages of Olympia. Close beside him his sister-spouse sat on her throne.

The goddess was of stone; she had on her head a leaf-wreathed polos, and her hair, covered with a net, fell in waves over her forehead in a row of flat locks. Beneath the high brows gazed dilated eyes of white and blue enamel. The thin straight lips dipped into two dimples

185

at the corners of the mouth and created a smile which imparted to the full, oval features a look of kindly benevolence. The gold-worked polos, the red net and the slightly less red hair gleamed down upon them.

The rest of her form was hidden by her peplos, the heavy embroideries of which hung down to the feet of the statue.

"Perhaps you have seen the house in the market-place at Elis," suggested the kleiduchos, "where the sixteen women live. They are the priestesses. There they weave and embroider for the goddess the peplos which they bring every fourth year at the time of the Heraia, Hera's festival. The old garment is handed over to the treasury. And here is the discus of Iphitos."

A more important thing could not have been uttered in a less indifferent voice. Both competitors bent over the bronze plate lying on the tripod. The words on the precious metal were embedded in it like the human voice in a dark tempestuous night and its faintest lines came to the surface, as it were, like an unintelligible whisper. The letters, fitting each other like cogs, ran around the rim of the discus and what appeared as the beginning of one word would turn out to be the end of another, which again had no beginning. The eyes, becoming tear-filled, could see nothing more. Ergoteles touched the discus with his hand. When he withdrew it Sotion grasped the bronze as if he were going to lift it. But he only held his palms on it, over the whole area of the writing, like a priest, one would say, ratifying an oath of alliance.

"Come," said the kleiduchos, "I will show you the chest of Kypselos."

"Oh, bury yourself in it!" shouted Sotion.

Olympia was full of sounds. At the well the grating of the buckets was heard; somewhere the cisterns were opened and the water gushed out into the channels which carried it to every part of the Altis. In the corner between the wall and the prytaneion, the Xyleus, or woodcutter of the sacred precinct, was cutting stakes of white poplar wood equal in length to the traditional measure. The carts conveying sand to the stadium creaked along. A score or so of people were levelling the furrowed ground, supervised by Hysmon. He was now walking about the part already strewn over and every few paces he dug his finger into the earth, measuring the depth of the layer of sand.

"The old man is feeling if it is fit for our bare feet," whispered Sotion.

By every path people were coming, competitors with their relations. Hysmon drove them away so that the work might not be disturbed. He told them to go and see the stone of Bybon or the statues.

The stone of Bybon lay adjacent to the Heraion. It was a rugged block of red sandstone on which was carved the inscription:

Bybon, seizing me with one hand, flung me over his head.

On the stone there were two clefts, apparently hand-holds. This and that one succeeded in lifting it as high as his knee or his thigh, but no one could throw it freely. Ikkos, who had come along from somewhere, witnessing this pastime, exclaimed:

"Get Gerenos!"

As a matter of fact the Naukratite was at hand and

without a word approached the stone. He could not thrust his whole palm into the cleft, scarcely three fingers fitted in. He jerked the stone up as high as his chest, then twisted it in his hand and, at the moment when it seemed that it would slip out of his grasp, he propelled it with a sudden fling a few paces away.

Ikkos turned to Eurymenes:

"Take heed that he does not break your bones while wrestling."

Alkimidas came running up. "Leave that. I'll show you something better."

Immediately they followed him, tossed about like leaves in a wind, on this day of idleness.

"This is an ancestor of mine," said the Aeginetan.

It was Praxidamas, a victor in the fifty-ninth Olympiad. Hewn out of the trunk of a cypress-tree, with dark streaks all over and roughened by the rains, the wind and the sun, he remained immobile with his fists pressed to his thighs, boxing straps painted in thick gilt on his hands. In the centre of his forehead was a furrow-like fissure, three-quarters of a century old. Alkimidas hoped that a likeness to himself would be seen in him. There was none. The wooden Praxidamas had a round head, a broad face stretched by a meaningless smile, and he stared with prominent eyes of blue glass which gave them a hard, almost lifeless lustre. He resembled only Rhexibios of Opous, a champion younger than he by two Olympiads, whom he had never seen during his lifetime, and who now stood next to him on a neighbouring plinth shaped out of the bole of a fig-tree.

Walking onwards along the fringe of the sacred grove

from the house of Oinomaos, they came across rows of statues whose pedestals bore names that still lived in the memory of the competitors. They repeated them aloud like a litany: Phrikias of Pelinna, Eutelidas of Sparta, Phanas of Pellene, Damaretos of Heraia, Milon of Croton. On all sides gazed the same protuberant eyes, the same full lips of red copper smiled, the hair was done up in the same way, in stars and ringlets over the forehead and hanging stiffly behind as in statues of the Egyptian gods. The heavy-armed runners were recognised by their helmets, the discus was the emblem of the pentathletes, occasionally a boxer or a wrestler made a cautious and timid gesture, the smothered whisper of the strength that had given him the prize.

Stiffly upright figures predominated, with trunks much too long and chests too narrow, like men of an extinct race; put into the shade of time by the veteran Hermes, who was wrapped in a chiton and a chlamys with a helmet on his head and holding a lamb under his arm. But look, the Metapontian Zeus was pacing with great strides into the present day. In his extended right hand he held the thunderbolt, on his left palm sat the eagle with partly spread wings, as if the deity's impetuous motion was starting him off on a flight. After him came other statues of shapes more and more rounded; they were less lifeless, every now and then, with a thrill of delight, somebody would observe the exquisite muscles of the abdomen, the firm-set knee, the bold curve of a thigh. On two pedestals there were horses in a pose which portrayed their frenzied impatience to start. They glittered in new bronze with sky-blue manes standing out like the crest of a helmet. Finally, the gigantic Heracles, with a bow and club, was hastening to some battle in the pose of the Phoenician Melkart.

The lofty grove with its figures of men and gods was paved with a profusion of stone slabs, embedded in every vacant spot. On them were engraved inscriptions concerning the Olympian laws and privileges, words of gratitude or praise. Towns and tribes announced treaties and alliances, the Anaitans and the Metapians pledged themselves to a fifty years' truce, the mighty Selinus took under its protection the exiles of Megara; on a slab, darkened through age, the Eleans and the Heraians concluded a hundred years' peace. All this was closed, like the last word of a hymn, by an immense block of marble which bore a list of the peoples that had fought at Plataeae.

They stood at the edge of the processional way, immediately behind which lay the wall of the Altis. They were filled with a feeling that something was wanting. One temple, a small number of chapels, a few statues, some scores of altars, hiding the common gravel beneath the fresh lime—this could be borne like a light travelling-bag containing just the most indispensable things.

The perfection of their bodies did not find satisfaction in the manifestation of this art which could not equal their shapeliness.

But two paces away from their disillusion, in the heart of the grove, Libon of Elis, an architect, was talking with the secretary of the Olympic Council:

". . . to cut out these trees. Six planes, eight poplars, thirteen olives. Kallistephanos will then be under the opisthodomos. The temple will have a length of two hundred feet; that excludes the entrance terrace which, by the way, will be quite outside beyond the grove. I will show you the drawings."

Above humble old Olympia there was being built a new Olympia in space, in the blue void, in that magnetic vacuum where, quick as lightning, the idea of a new epoch was born. A new era was dawning, men's minds were acquiring fresh vigour as they would from an abundance of ozone. There spread an indescribable gladness akin to a great bliss, accruing from regained harmony, from the victorious war, from an overflowing fund of energy; a new design for life was being sought. Its presence was felt everywhere, at certain moments a deep impression reigned that forms thronged on all sides and it would seem that the real word was dominated by a world not yet come into being. The people who were to create it were hidden in the crowd. Perikles had turned his twentieth year. Phidias, Myron, Polykleitos were walking about Olympia unrecognised. In mountain depths the marble was entombed that would be liberated to-morrow from its stony sleep; there in the quarries of Pentelikon every particle of the Parthenon lay waiting; young beauty was maturing in the snowy lap of the island of Paros.

CHAPTER V

THE SPRIG OF WILD OLIVE

ON the next day at dawn an offering was made to Hestia.

In the prytaneion, which in each Greek settlement was of paramount importance, there burned the *akamaton pyr*—the unwearying, the never-extinguished fire. Watchful and undefiled, it represented the virgin goddess who, like a fixed star, sits in the centre of the Olympian house of the gods. Begotten in the dawn of the ages by the boring or rubbing of two pieces of wood, it could not be regenerated in any way other than by the one original act. The white poplar logs, burning day and night, had raised a hillock of ashes that must be swept up only once a year, in the month of Elaphios, collected and carried away to the altar of Zeus. The wind which poured in through the slit in the ceiling was prevented from blowing the ashes about by a kerb of heavy stones that surrounded the ash heap. The rectangular chamber which contained the altar was narrow and high, and black as a chimney with soot and smoke.

The priest rearranged the half-charred pieces of wood which had lain over the embers during the night. Uncertainty as to whether the small glowing bits retrieved from the ashes would glimmer up and burst into flame always caused a moment of uneasiness. Dried olive leaves were thrown in and while they crinkled and rolled up, the soothsayer listened eagerly for their dying unintelligible whisper. On the fresh handful of leaves a drop of olive-oil fell; it hissed and there ascended a column of pungent fumes thin as a thread; the priest bent down and with his breath roused the dormant flame. Under his puffing lips the fringe of the fire flickered. He then spread his arms out and with the rest of his breath broke into a hymn. He sang slowly and distinctly, that the time-worn sound of the words might not be obscured; he invoked all the gods, Hellenic and alien, the demigods and their consorts, the heroes of migrations, of wars and of conquests.

Meanwhile, at the other end of the Altis, in the southern wing of the Bouleuterion, the competitors were standing before the hellanodikai. They were separated by a row of columns which ran through the centre of the hall. Kapros, sitting between two "nomophylakes", presided over the board of judges. In his hand he held the leukoma, a white tablet, from which he read out the names and particulars of the competitors. For the first time they heard his voice, crisp and pointed, like the voice of a commander. Moments passed, and nobody could keep from quaking at the thought that for some reason or other his name might not be called out. Only those who had already won Olympic victories were at ease. They stood in the front rank, and their passionless faces stood out like stars in this agitated firmament. In the midst of the white chlamydes of this gathering the ornate coats of the princes showed up clearly.

The list opened with the name of Astylos. The triple victor was enrolling for the armed race.

"Euthymos, son of Astykles, from the Italian Lokri—boxing," announced Kapros.

Theagenes, when his name was called, promptly interjected: "Pancration!"

Ikkos nudged Kallias, who was standing beside him. The Athenian nodded and attempted to smile.

Then came the turn of the princes, each of whom had to his credit several wins in the races, and finally those of the Kleian gymnasium answered to their names. At the name of the Spartan Ladas, who had arrived last, the hellanodikai held a whispered conference. For he needed a few days more to complete the required month of practice in Elis. Kapros leaned over to one of the "guardians of the law", who was heard to say:

"There is no law that exercises should be carried out in Olympia, it is only a custom."

"A custom which has, nevertheless, long since become a law," said Onomastos. "Otherwise how in the world would it be possible to sift the chaff from the grains?"

"That," said the veteran, pointing at Ladas, "you can see at a glance."

"He has already been a champion in Nemea and in the Isthmus," intimated another.

Kapros decided with a slight nod, lifted his head and glanced at the runner. Ladas took this for a question, and said:

"The long distance."

But Kapros did not remove his gaze from him; for a moment he focused his head with an attentive look, full of compassion. The Spartan paled. When the competitors began to disperse, he still could not calm down:

"What did he see in me?" he asked Gerenos.

The Naukratian halted as if nonplussed by the question and shrugged his shoulders:

"Kapros," he said, "is of the family of the Klytiades, the seers."

But both became submerged in the murmuring that surrounded them. Sodamos whispered that someone's name had not been called. It was not certain who, yet there was a feeling that a name, which at this moment nobody could remember, had been omitted.

From the steps of the Bouleuterion they entered the crowd which made way for them.

Between one wing and the other of the building lay a roofless hall surrounded on three sides by a wall and open to the east. It formed a rigid quadrilateral of nothing but stone, stone walls and stone floor; only in the centre an altar stood. This, not being white-washed, exposed the pale-bluish grey of the lime formed by the myriads of snails still to be seen in the shells that time had not digested. Black spots of blood, which the rains have not washed away, which the sun has not absorbed, remained from the last Olympiad.

At this altar ruled Zeus Horkios, the patron of oaths.

The priest had lit the fire with a firebrand from the altar of Hestia, and now he added fresh fuel. The competitors entered and ranged themselves on both sides of the altar, the men and boys keeping separate. The former threw back their chlamydes, so that the right arm was bared and free. The boys' arms remained covered, as these were not to be used, and their chlamydes fell evenly down. The oath would be taken in their name by their fathers, or, if anyone had no father, by his paternal uncle or elder brother or some more distant relative. These stood behind the group of boys. Near the third wall the trainers waited.

With the entrance of the hellanodikai a hum ran between the Bouleuterion and the barrow of Hippodameia. The rhabduchi vociferously demanded a clear passage, they brandished their sticks and finally succeeded in clearing a wide lane between two rows of people. At the far end a grunting was heard. The attendants of the priests were leading along a wild boar.

At the altar the animal, giving way to a queer foreboding, flinched a pace backwards. Two men were holding it by chains fastened to the complex collar fixed round the groins of the forelegs, the nape and part of the belly. The boar wriggled about, dealt random blows with its tusks and finally wedged its cloven hoofs into the ground. But it was chiefly determined not to go nearer the altar and did not notice that the chains were lifting it up. The forelegs, it is true, had lost their support and were already suspended in the air, but with its hind legs the boar held on spiritedly. Fully intent on this purpose, it did not even emit a squeal when the knife pierced its unguarded throat. It fell with a muffled groan and immediately the legs stiffened. The harness and chains were removed, the belly was opened, and the priest cut out the lungs, the heart and the liver. He tore off a portion of the hide, wrapped in it the bloody flesh and put this on the fire, which received it with a crackle and a hiss, giving off the peculiar effluvium of burning leather.

The hellanodikai drew nearer to the altar, and Kapros turned to the competitors: "Prior to taking the oath," he said, "let each one search his soul to make certain that he stands before the god taintless, and sure that he will not offend him with the most trifling lie. It will be no disgrace should anybody walk away from the altar, it will be rather a proof of his honesty and fear of the wrath of the god." A tremor passed through the white-clad groups. Here and there someone blenched, some of the boys with rigidly tensed lips looked sideways, spell-bound, it seemed, by the dark sheen of the bronze colossus of Zeus, the upper half of whose frame loomed above the wall of the Altis, with eyes wide open and in his hand a thunderbolt ready to hurl.

A prolonged silence prevailed. The hellanodikes commenced reading out the names of the competitors. Those who were called stepped out from the group and stood in pairs facing the altar. After the last name the hellanodikes pronounced the formula of the oath, according to which each one swore that he was worthy of the Games, that he was of Hellenic parentage, free born, that no innocent blood was on his head, that no fine due to the gods or to the temples burdened him, that he took up his rôle as a competitor conscientiously after ten months of practice, that in the contest in which he was engaging he would not resort to any foul means, that he would not seduce his opponent with a bribe, that he was submitting his endeavour to merit the praise of the god who would recompense him or leave him unrewarded according to his will.

All raised their right arms and some said briefly: "I swear," while others added: "If I have sworn sincerely, may it happen as I desire, and if falsely, let bad luck beset me," or some such other words. Some stepped out of the row and pronounced the oath at the altar itself, touching the heated blood-stained stone with their palms.

With the boys the ceremony lasted longer. First, they were summoned by name, then he who took the oath for them presented himself to the god, and finally, placing his hand on the head of the young contestant, with his own life and happiness he would vouch for the worthiness of his ward.

Last of all the swearing-in of the hellanodikai was accomplished. Having first purified themselves with a few drops of the blood of the offering (dipping their hands into the bowels of the boar), they repeated in turn the words which the President of the Council read out to them: that they would judge according to the law of the gods and with a good conscience; that they would not be misled by any pretexts, persuasions, threats or bribes; that they would not divulge the reasons upon which their judgment was based.

Fresh fuel was added and the raging fire digested the remnants of the offering. The boar, which lay lacerated in a pool of blood, was to be removed. The meat of the animal over which the oaths were taken was untouchable. The priests' attendants lifted it from the floor and bore it to the Alpheios; he was to give it back to the sea, to soundless eternity. But two dogs from the camp, tracking along the blood trail, plunged into the water and seized the flesh where it was caught among the branches of an old myrtle-tree that floated towards the river.

All along the paths of the sacred grove people surged in the direction of the stadium, although the boys' events did not start till the afternoon. The bank separating the track from the hippodrome was already occupied; at the eastern end, where the stadium encroached upon the river-valley, benches, stalls and folding chairs were brought. But the greatest bustle concentrated on the slope of Kronion. People rushed up it as on a day of flood. Feet would lose their hold on the pine-needles strewn on the hillside; someone would fall headlong and trip up those who were standing lower. Branches that were grasped would break off with a crack. Those who managed to clamber up into trees were hilariously noisy on their safe and shady perches.

Shade here was greatly appreciated. It was broiling; the month of Parthenios was still full summer. Of all the seasons this one seemed the least fitted for the gathering of a huge crowd to witness a whole day's spectacle. But such an arrangement had been come to in the primeval ages by agricultural folk. Harvests had just been reaped, the corn had been threshed and poured into the barns. Man had peace up to the middle of September, until the time when Bootes appears in the heavens and sets out with his star-formed wain to gather fruit, wine and olives.

Rigid custom forbade that the head be covered with either a hat or any substitute. But all wore wreaths, while some would plait flowers and leaves into cap-like shapes which adequately shielded them from the sun's rays.

The undulating slope rested on a terrace which fell in nine steps towards the Altis. This terrace had on it small buildings resembling temples, but their façades, embellished with columns, looked towards the south, which meant that they were not the abode of the gods. They were the treasuries in which the more valuable votive offerings or appliances were kept. The inscriptions on the architraves specified whose possession they were: Gela,

Metapontum, Byzantium, Sikyon, Samos, Epidamnos, illustrated on this confined area the wide expanse of the Greek world; the town Sybaris, in ruins for scores of years, was recalled to memory on one building, and the new treasury of the Syracusans, like a trophy, recounted their victory over Carthage. Coloured cornices ran along the buildings; palmettes of painted terra-cotta bloomed in the sun and the gutters ended in gargoyles. Sculptures on the pediment of the Megarian repository illustrated the Gigantomachy, and the treasure-house of the Cyrenaeans depicted the nymph Cyrene in combat with a lion. Every brick of their walls had been brought from the fatherland; there were parts that had been completely finished at home, and these furnished specimens of the native earth, an obvious symbol of concord with the Olympic god.

Gradually they were being occupied. To these magnificent boxes only those representatives had access whose governments were the possessors of the buildings. In cases where this right was extinct or was questioned, the final decision lay with the Council. In addition, there were the various obligations of hospitality to be repaid and these were now revealed in bows, amicable gestures and words which commemorated the affiliation of tribes, colonies and heroes.

Men of authority and wealth moved leisurely with heavy tread, as if in sandals of gold; their arms were encumbered by ample coats, and their fixed smile produced an illusion of reliability and friendliness. From the hillside the crowd gazed at these personages as at characters in the opening scene of a drama: the casual, emotionless meetings, with a chorus in the background voicing its belief in love and righteousness. But it was a pageantry worth witnessing, if the mutual relations of these people were known, if it was realised that the one was conspiring the downfall of the other, that for Hieron the sun would lose its brightness were he to be told that old Theron of Akragas would not die poverty-stricken and in ignominy. Hieron, however, with a smile on his sickly face, walked between Theron and the latter's son Thrasydaios, between two poisoned daggers, conducted them to the treasure-house of Gela, returned and greeted on his way the gentlemen of Selinus, whom he wished to see in irons.

From below, climbing up the steps, new groups continued to arrive that attracted no crowds. These were people to whom the ends of the earth lay open. The ships sailing under their banners, the warehouses at their ports, the thousands of slaves in their fields, made a way for them, and those who personally were of little importance depended on the influence their governments wielded. Of the architheoroi, more than one gave the impression that on his head, like the goddess Kybele, he carried the towers of his city as a crown.

The Macedonian king, however, seated himself humbly on one of the lower steps of the terrace. When he was noticed there, a murmur of approval spread along the hillside. For many this was a rallying-sign. Uncertain whether they would be invited to the treasuries, the dignitaries of lesser governments accepted with pleasure these places which had achieved distinction through his presence. Members of the Council and priests collected together and, having secured seats for themselves, stood about conversing, for there was still time enough before undergoing the discomfort of these rough and pointed stones. Voices resounded from the terrace, and names covered with renown were to be heard. Someone cried out: "Pindar!" and when hundreds of eyes looked where he was pointing, one man here and there succeeded in catching a glimpse of a serious-looking personage with a flowing beard, who disappeared into the treasury of Gela.

A tumultuous noise possessed the mountain slope whenever any former victor was recognised. At the sound of their names they turned towards the crowd showing the faces of youths with their first beard, of men in the prime of life whose statues stood in the sacred grove, and of a few veterans who passed by like phantoms of the dark ages. Old Damaretos of Heraea evoked great excitement.

He had been the first victor in the race in armour at the sixty-fifth Olympiad. The grand old man, hoary-bearded and with long hair which fell in several plaits on his shoulders, walked supported on the one side by his son Theopompos, the champion in the pentathlon, and on the other by his grandson Theopompos, who in the last Olympiad had won the wreath for wrestling. Strikingly alike in features and attitude, they somewhat resembled an oak whose fine old trunk divides into two strong boughs. Damaretos was a picture of the highest bliss that can be attained by man on this earth. Those who had seen him four years ago, when his grandson with a fresh wreath had approached him to lay it on his knees, were astonished at finding him still alive, as though this superabundant measure of the gods' favour was more than could be borne so long. The entire terrace stood up, all offering him their seats. He walked up the hillside and sat down amidst the Megarians, who happened to be the nearest.

The water from the reservoir above the Heraion was let out. The channel, coursing by way of the terrace, carried a swift stream between the lowest steps. From the top pitchers were immediately dispatched and returned, passed up from hand to hand. The dignitaries in the front rows became water-carriers. Nobody avoided this duty, and King Alexander worked the hardest. Huge supplies of water were accumulated and much was spilt on the way up. Disputes arose over vessels being exchanged. But suddenly everything became silent at the appearance of the hellanodikai emerging from the grove.

Kapros led the way and after him, two by two, eight others followed. Behind this crimson-clad group a long row of naked boys advanced, resembling a golden bar. Their eyes were fixed on the ground, watching their feet, in order not to overstep the measure. Behind the last pair the trainers, dressed in white, made their appearance. Dressed likewise in white, the remaining competitors brought up the rear. The trainers passed into an enclosure prepared for them near the altar of Hera, and the competitors surrounded the tent of the hellanodikai. Only the naked boys, like quarried bits of pale-coloured sandstone, stood motionless before the mound of Zeus, whose altar smoked with the remains of the morning's offering.

From the Heraion a tripod was brought out, and two men set it before the judges. The ground was uneven, the tripod oscillated, they moved it first in one direction and then in another until it got a firm footing. Then again there was a momentary pause, all gazing in the direction of the grove, the green face of which was that day filled with action like the stage of a theatre. From it stepped the theokolos, the chief priests in the season of the Games. At his side a boy carried a bunch of sprigs of wild olive and the golden knife with which he had cut them from the tree. This boy, an intended priest, was the son of one of the spondophoroi and had both parents living, for no one across whose path death's shadow had been cast was permitted to approach the sacred tree. In the centre of the scene the theokolos took the boy's hand to guide him, as it were, through this terrible void teeming with the glances of many thousands. Kapros took the knife and the sprigs from the boy and placed them on the tripod.

One of the hellanodikai read out names from the white tablet. Each man darted out from the rectangular formation which wavered and gaped to let him pass. Thereupon a herald proclaimed this same name and, turning to the spectators, asked if anyone was aware of any stain defiling it. So many investigations, so many inquiries had been made about each competitor, so many witnesses had been heard to prove his purity, yet here, even at this last moment each was exposed to suspicion and distrust in the eyes of the world! But the herald's words were answered by silence. Occasionally the name of one of the sixteen announced was repeated from somewhere in an undertone and many eyes would attempt to pick out in the distance who it was.

Not more than two or three of them showed full maturity; their figures had reached stalwart proportions which would, of course, develop and amplify further.

On others the contours were still too straight, the angles too sharp, their future curves and flexures could not be gauged. Only the legs, exercised by running, had formed in advance of other muscles, as with a tree which on the side facing the sun is loaded with ripe fruit whereas on the branches in the shade its fruit is still green.

Hysmon held out the urn to them. In it there were bone counters, on each of which a letter of the alphabet was inscribed. The competitors approached it with averted faces, dipped their hands into the vessel (the timid movement of the fingers in this dark depth can be imagined) and, having drawn their lot, handed it to the hellanodikes standing behind them. In this way each one was allotted a place in one of the four quartets.

The first set made for the starting-point, opposite to the altar of Zeus. Three hellanodikai, including Hysmon, accompanied them and took their seats under a tent pitched on the crest of the bank. Opposite, on a white sacrificial stone, sat a woman, the only one who had a right to be here at the season of the Games. She was the priestess of Demeter Chamyne—the living relic of a world long since extinct.

Guarded by her imperishable and incomprehensible right, she sat separated from the hellanodikai by the whole width of the stadium with the barrow of Endymion behind her.

The goddess she worshipped possessed no material shape. To justify her existence in the conception of the new era the deity was incorporated with Demeter, the goddess of the fructifying earth. But the etymology of time-honoured Chamyne's name revealed quite another significance: it means most probably that abyss into which death hurls human life. She was a screen for the ignorance, fear and defencelessness of a remote age. Chamyne—these few letters depict the futile and aim-less existence of the people of her time amid false im-pressions of the real nature of things and mystifications of their own making.

The boys lined up for the start, and the same voice which so often had electrified them into motion during the course of the exercises, the cry of Hysmon—"Apite!" —propelled them on to the stadium.

The sun, slightly declined from noon, cast their dwarfed flickering shadows under their feet. The hair of one of them, which was made up into a bundle behind the head, had come loose and now floated above his shining neck. The arms, moving like wings, flapped the air which glowed like a flame in its last breath. There! Someone has reached the line and, unable to check him-self, has run on a few paces more, but the trace of his foot with the oblong imprint of the great toe, deeper than that of the others, is observed at the goal.

The winner was a boy from Byzantium, and his native town hailed him with a burst of cheering. For the others his name signified nothing. Impatient calls for quiet were heard. The second quartet lined up at the start.

The heats were quickly over. Four streaks of sparkling flight like four lightning flashes, after each one a roar from the throng like thunder, and behold, there came a laden surcharged silence; under the cloudless heaven a human tempest gathered.

The winners of the fours proceeded to the final heat.

A swallow whistled past; on one of the trees the

branches swayed under the weight of an unquiet body; someone's rapid audible gulps, while drinking water, were heard. There hovered over the stadium a mute suspense.

The four boys got ready at the starting point; though all of them were victors, they were still fledglings of the track. The immensity of the moment weighed on them; they could not control a slight trembling; gooseflesh, beneath the layer of olive-oil, showed on their shoulders.

Hysmon bustled around them like a stork about to start its young on their first flight. Had it been possible, he would have said something, he would have encouraged them with a word or a pat on the back. But meanwhile he continued correcting their postures, pushing their feet up to the starting-line as if he were testing a bow-string.

"Apite!"

They wrenched themselves off the ground—now it all depended solely on them. They travelled with the velocity and the blindness of a stone that has been hurled down a precipice. Hysmon remained rooted to the spot stricken, as it were, by all their faults, which he either noticed or merely imagined to be there; an unusual uneasy feeling swept over him: could it be that he wished the whole quartet might carry off the prize?

And they, running as though they must fulfil this unreasonable desire, were already half-way along the track, now two-thirds, and all the time keeping exactly abreast, as if the line at the start was drawn across their chests and was speeding together with them!

The whole world was held in that balance of theirs, not a single breath disturbed the divine scales on which their fate, in a balance that remains unchanged, was being weighed.

All of a sudden the smooth surface of their progression creased in a sharp wrinkle and split where Glaukos was running. This effort caused a thrill affecting all. A magnetic spark coursed from the first steps of the terrace up to the hill-top. Everyone felt the pressure of the tremendous determination that was being applied in the slight body of the boy from Chios.

Voices here and there ejaculated his name. Taken up instantly, this grew into a shout which tore into the space separating him from his rivals; and becoming ever stronger, more passionate and fierce, it kept in his wake and like a flood tide bore him to the goal.

There remained yet one moment, when the uproar whirled around him, and he, with his arm raised, his last action in the run, resembled a wrecked ship calling for help; ultimately he sank down, as if actually drowning, at the steps of the altar and the huge wave of the voices ebbed away and abruptly ran dry in the sand of the stadium.

Silence prevailed. The boy's behaviour was puzzling. The rules required that the competitor, however decisive his victory might be, should stand among his rivals and wait until called to the tent of the hellanodikai. One section of the spectators, those whose seats were westwards from the altar, could not understand his disappearance. The whole terrace, however, and the entire hillside from the edge of the track kept him in sight.

Look, he has sat down on the lowest step of the altar, he lifts his right leg, rests the ankle on his left thigh and bends over his foot. Just under his little toe is a thorn, he takes it out, and a drop of blood glistens on the surface.

At which spot and when did the track prick him with this thorn? Did it happen before he had detached himself from the quartet, or in the last few strides? Nobody knows. Until his soul returned to consciousness after the completion of the course, he himself had no idea of it.

Glaukos, sitting bent with his chest retracted under the arch of his back, was so diminutive and humble-looking that, in place of victory in the stadium, it seemed there lay behind him an ordinary unploughed strip of field on which he had been chasing a butterfly. With his finger he kept on rubbing the drop of blood on the sole of his foot. Then he got up and took his position at the end of the quartet, of which he was the shortest. No excitement ruffled his serious oval countenance. It looked smaller because of his thick hair which fell over his eyebrows and left exposed a small triangular portion of the forehead.

"That is a brave boy," said Ikkos to Sotion, "but the best of the quartet is Leagros. Glaukos had time to rest while two heats were being run, whereas Leagros had the final heat, immediately after his own. Furthermore, Glaukos is the lightest and his feet do not sink so deep into the sand."

"But you don't know whether Leagros would have completed the run with a thorn in his foot."

Sodamos burst out laughing:

"How amusing that little Xenophon is! Would you believe it, he made a vow to his Corinthian Aphrodite—fifty girls if he won! I have repeatedly told him that those girls of his are not yet born."

"He keeps moving his lips as if he were quarrelling with his Aphrodite," said Telesikrates.

"Let him alone," says Skamadros, "he will make a good athlete yet."

But Gryllos interrupted the conversation:

"I say, watch Hysmon!"

The hellanodikes hurried along with huge strides from the starting-point, leaving two of his colleagues behind. It was only too evident how deeply that thorn had hurt him. His lips trembled. Halting in front of the tent, he could not utter a word, though he had already raised his hand. Kapros promptly calmed him:

"Of course, order fresh sand to be strewn."

Hysmon then summoned one of the rhabduchi with so hoarse a voice that the poor unfortunate could hear in it the grating of a prison bolt. The attendant sped towards the Bouleuterion as fast as his legs would carry him, to the intense amusement of the throng, which roared as he went as it had roared for the competitors.

"Glaukos!" called Kapros and stood up, while the boy approached the tripod on which lay the olive sprigs. From these the hellanodikes took two, bound them with a red ribbon and placed this wreath on Glaukos's head. The herald proclaimed the first victor of the seventy-sixth Olympiad, announcing the name of the boy, that of his father and of his country, the island of Chios.

His country descended upon him. A group of citizens, among whom Glaukos's father was, detached itself from the audience and surrounded him. They were joined by many Athenians, for the isle of Chios belonged to Athens.

Glaukos took off the wreath and handed it to his father. He had fought at Salamis, where his right arm

210

had been severed by a Persian axe at the moment when
he was about to board one of the Persian ships. Not
wishing to take the wreath with his left hand, which
would be a bad omen, he made a sign to his brother. The
uncle accepted the wreath and put it back on the boy's
head. Thereafter others pressed round him, they fastened
white and red ribbons about his arms, his chest, his
thighs; into his hair they stuffed flowers; soon he resembled the statue of a god decorated on a feast day.

The crowd cheered. From the top of the hill green
sprigs were thrown into the air; they fell on those sitting
along the terrace. Every now and then a more vigorous
clamour would burst out. This would travel from Kronion
up to the heights of Pisa; it could not be stemmed even
by the river. It resounded beyond—on those high ranges
of Triphylia across the Alpheios echoed the voices of
women who were permitted to watch the Games from this
distance.

Meanwhile the cart with the sand arrived. Hysmon
ordered it to be strewn over an area at the end of the
track only, a hundred feet or thereabouts in front of the
altar, on the site reserved for the boxing and wrestling
contests. During this part of the Games the rest of the
stadium was not utilised, an opportunity of which advantage was immediately taken. Those whose seats were on
the side beyond the start drew nearer with their benches
and stools; many squatted down on the sand itself. In
the front row was Glaukos with his party. Near the start
only the priestess of Chamyne remained, who from her
desolate altar saw nothing but the lifeless track.

The boys taking part in the boxing were called. There
were but six of them. Sodamos was astonished:

"By Heracles! I had never imagined they would thin them like that. On various occasions in Elis I reckoned their number at about a hundred." Sotion, who remembered many of them, expressed sympathy for two or three pairs.

"It's useless dwelling on it," chimed in Ikkos; "as it is, they will take up enough time. Boys are capable of frisking about until the evening."

He was mistaken. The first pair—Protolaos versus Alkimidas—forthwith set to in earnest. The punches were like lightning and the side-stepping like lightning too. Constantly attacking each other, they were never far apart. Their feet traced an irregular circle or ellipse on the sand as if a magnetic field held them in its orbit.

First Alkimidas broke loose from the maze of blows and with parted lips stepped a few paces away as if he had popped out of cold water. But Protolaos immediately pulled him back into the whirlpool.

Alkimidas led only with his right fist, the left served him exclusively to guard; he had not the courage to use it in attack because hampered by the annoying memory of the hellanodikes punishing him for striking with the left palm before he had managed to clench it. Protolaos, free in his movements, jabbed him with a left hook. From Alkimidas's nose blood streamed forth, and with the additional punches it splashed round his lips and spread like a red flower in the centre of his face.

A fiery spark flared up in the crowd like tinder. Alkimidas was pummelled not by Protolaos's fists alone, for the yells of the spectators smote him also. These beset and harried him, the whole world was against him until, completely winded, he finally raised his hand, admitting defeat.

The night was in his head, in his ears, in his eyes, but behold, a smile lit up his face: Alkimidas's soul, quivering with the delight of the contest, peered out of his exhausted body as does the sun from behind clouds.

Of the three winners, Protolaos, Pytheas and Agesidamos, Pytheas drew the lucky bye which was viewed with contempt. For during the whole bout of the Mantinean with the Lokrian he could sit quietly and rest, and would subsequently have to contend with an exhausted opponent. But Pytheas, the son of the rich and mighty Lampon, was not at all perturbed. He was one of those who knew full well the worth of everything, a man who was aware that each and every thing most valued is easier to acquire by chance, through the smile of fate and, where possible, by artifice. Half of their affluence and importance the Psalychids owed to opportunities such as these, where human judgment could not be depended upon.

And so Pytheas gave himself up with an easy mind to the attention of his aleiptes. Both belonged to the small group which had remained faithful to Ikkos. They imitated him up to the limits of absurdity, and even now, not heeding this tempestuous world which surrounded them, they set about their preparation.

The aleiptes first sponged Pytheas, then sprinkled him with water and lastly rubbed him over with fresh olive-oil. All through this process he endeavoured to place himself so that Pytheas was shaded from the sun. The boy thought he would like a drink; the aleiptes brought him water, but not even a drop did he permit him to swallow;

Pytheas must only rinse his mouth. Not knowing whether massaging would be appropriate at this time, he passed his hands along Pytheas's body with the movement of an Egyptian physician. Maybe he would have put him to sleep in the end, had not a sudden shout of the onlookers wrenched them from their magic.

Timasarchos was defeated. He had bruised knees, evidently he had fallen. His aleiptes, Melesias, the renowned "trainer of champions" foamed with rage. He wrapped him in a towel so fiercely that it seemed he wanted to choke him.

Agesidamos, walking up to his trainer, passed Pytheas, fanning him with the breath of his hot body; the strap on his left hand had come loose and he had barely time to readjust it when the herald announced the last bout.

It looked like a long encounter. Pytheas had made up his mind to take advantage of his freshness and to tire his opponent without hitting out. He kept himself beyond reach, ever and again he would side-step, quick and elusive, deaf to the cries of "Coward!" with which it was hoped to goad him into closer range. At the start, Agesidamos was beguiled by this play, he pursued Pytheas frenziedly, but afterwards he took his stand on one spot and waited. The encouraging smile of the spectators flowed around him like a stream of water.

The Aeginetan stood two paces away from Agesidamos, perplexed for the moment. The caution with which he began to approach evoked fresh outbursts. Smarting with shame, as if lashed by a whip, Pytheas threw himself on the Lokrian. Agesidamos kept him at arm's length, and promptly took the offensive himself. The Aeginetan parried admirably. But Agesidamos was so swift, so startling, so zealous, that Pytheas, getting dazed, retreated more and more.

The Olympic stadium had seldom before witnessed what now followed. Those who had seen Pytheas's previous encounters and victories could not have been prepared for this. For look, he had halted, he had crouched down and put both hands over his head to protect it! This attitude of hopeless fear, for which boys were beaten in the palestra, was something so incomprehensible that many thought it was a cunning trick. The spectators became silent, waiting for the surprise. Agesidamos himself, with his fists ready to feint and lead, hesitated like a dog facing a hedgehog that has rolled itself up.

It was then, Ilas, that you reaped fame immortal. It was then that you joined, for all time, your name with that of your pupil when you thundered out to Agesidamos: "Hit from below!"

Agesidamos heard this shout and as if by an inspiration he connected with Pytheas's unguarded chin. Blood spouted from the smashed jaw, his legs tottered, Lampon's son reeled and dropped. The Lokrian had a right to strike once again; he bent down—but suddenly he opened his fist and with the same hand that had vanquished the adversary he raised and supported his opponent.

What is there left of the cheering, the clapping, the excitement, even of many thousands of people? True, it exerts a potent spell, singular and momentous, but ultimately it fades away into the infinity of time. Nothing impedes the sound-waves that, as ever-spreading ripples, disperse outwards into space; everlasting, but lost to the ears of man. Those which on that day resounded with

Agesidamos's name still murmur somewhere in the furthest reaches of the cosmos and are as irretrievable as the dust on the magnificent body which was then the subject of admiration and rapture.

Nevertheless, here stands a monument on which there still echoes the tone of that sweltering afternoon of the 18th of August in the year 476 B.C.:

A time there is when men most need the winds; a time when they need the rains from heaven, the watery children of the cloud. And when effort attains its goal, they need honey-sweet songs, earnest of fame to come, trusty witness of their worth.

Imperishable is the fame of Olympic victors. And I, O Agesidamos, son of Archestratos, lay my song by thy golden wreath in honour of thy victory.

That is Pindar's ode, every word of which had its being in him that day, when he sat in the treasury of Gela beside his old friend Theron of Akragas, and stood up to shake the hand of his young friend Agesidamos, of the Epizephyrian Lokrians. Agesidamos was introduced by his father, Archestratos, who, turning to the prince, said:

"Son of Ainesidemos, I have heard that after the Games Pindar goes with you. If you permit it, I shall beg of him to sacrifice part of that time in my house."

"I shall come with a ship for you," said Agesidamos to Pindar.

The boy, begirt with wreath and ribbons, smelled of verdure and of the arena. The rosy stripes of the boxing straps were still on his hands, and on the column against which he leaned the greasy trace of olive-oil remained.

Meanwhile, from the slopes of the foothills a carriage came in sight, driving along the Alpheios. It travelled very swiftly in a cloud of dust. There glistened in the sun the fittings on the carriage and the harness of the horses, over whom the long whip waved incessantly. Nearing the camp, its pace slackened and the carriage disappeared among the tents.

Who could it be?

In this question was framed all the uneasiness that descends on a house, late in the evening, when all the inmates are gathered together and suddenly someone's footsteps are heard in the courtyard. The memory of the last Olympiad was revived, when the roads were full of grievous tidings and panic. The man who made this unexpected appearance belonged to those very days.

He was now passing by the Bouleuterion, having left behind a party of slaves who watched him from a distance. Soon the trees of the Grove hid him. Thousands of eyes watched the spot where all its paths had their outlet. For a while he must have lost his way there, because he appeared from the side of Pelops's barrow. He was recognised immediately. No voice was raised, mute attention continued to follow him, it seemed the crowd was examining his features as if to count the white strands which the last four years had put into the magnificent black beard so well acquainted with the breezes of Salamis. The people from the colonies, however, did not know who it was, and the name of Themistokles began to spread in a swelling whisper.

He stood still and raised his head, inclining it slightly sideways, as if he were trying to discern the theme of those murmurs; then he lifted his arm on high in greeting.

217

A cheer answered him. Unisonous at first, it grew later into a din of voices which accompanied him up to the steps of the terrace.

He could not get any further. The people who rose up to salute him formed a wall, and he stood beside it shaking scores of hands. He embraced King Alexander; they had so much to tell each other that not so much as a word could they summon. Others, however, smothered him with questions, in answer to which he nodded or smiled. Catching sight of Hydna standing on one of the steps higher up, he gave her his hand above several heads.

The entire hillside swooped onto the terrace. The swarm overran the treasuries, branches cracked and water-vessels were trampled under foot. The men who had been at Salamis pressed round their leader: "Do you remember me?" They shouted out their names and details of the battle. Each one who on that day had sighted him from his ship was positive that the leader had seen him too.

A violent surge brought Hieron on the scene. Reluctant at first, he had finally moved of his own accord towards Themistokles.

"Why didn't you come then?" said the Athenian. "You are four years late."

The Syracusan tyrant managed to smile:

"We should not have found room in the gulf."

"I would have made a little room for you on the open sea."

These "winged words", swift as a swallow, flew through the gathering which received them with a deafening outburst of laughter.

Gradually, step by step, Themistokles climbed to the top, a great concourse behind him.

Nobody paid the slightest heed to order now. Many had lost their places and it was out of the question to think of regaining them. They stayed on the terrace, transforming it into a huge, littered, nomadic camp-site. The princes and the oligarchs, jostled into the vestibules of the treasuries, might have been prisoners. The crowd vociferated with bold delight, as though the arrival of this leader of democracy had brought about a sudden change.

Here and there, however, calls for quiet made themselves heard. A part of the spectators had remained faithful to the Games, which were going on as arranged. The boys' wrestling had started long before. There was no means of knowing who was paired against whom, for the herald's voice was lost in the general hubbub. The contestants were recognised only by their fellow-countrymen and these tried to bawl out their names above the din. They were not heard. There was no power that could tear the masses from their self-glorification.

It was only much later that they became silent of their own accord, exhausted with excitement and drunk with words. They were plunged into a blissful feeling of satiety, having rationed out Salamis like bread.

The sun hid behind the ranges, the valley was steeped in the colour of new wine. From the altar of Zeus there fell a shadow, on the edge of which two boys were wrestling like two spirits representing day and night. At last one of them fell on his knees; of his whole body only a part of the arms up to the elbows was in the light; but

219

the other thrust and finally tumbled him into the shade.

On the lit portion of the stadium, in the scarlet hues of the setting sun, within the blaze of cheering, stood Theognetos of Ægina, champion of the boy wrestlers.

CHAPTER VI

SOTION'S DAY

THE second day of the Games started on the hippodrome. It was preceded by a night full of stir and
anxiety. Those who had horses did not sleep for fear
the grooms might neglect something. A thousand times
over the same questions would be heard: How much
wheat had they been given, when did they last have a
feed, did they betray any signs of weakness? The stable
attendants implored their masters not to waken the
animals, which needed rest. A whispered "Hush!" was
then heard, and everybody became silent or talked in
whispers, as in a sick-room. Suddenly someone or other,
seized with an ominous feeling, would snatch up a lan-
tern and rush off to inspect the stalls or to make sure that
strangers were not loitering about the stable. Some owners
spent the night beside their horses.

Hieron took his bay steed, Pherenikos, to his tent. In
the middle of the night he awakened his brother-in-
law Chromios, so that he might go and keep guard
over the four horses in the team that was engaging in
the chariot race. At the last moment, however, he
stopped him.

"Is there no one here who understands charms?"

"There may be one among the Carthaginians,"
answered Chromios. "Why, what for?"

"Theron, for sure, has buried a tablet, a magic tablet thwarting our horses. Something must be done about it. There is still time before moon-set."

"There is still time"—Chromios was impatient—"for you to get some sleep."

Hieron could not sleep, but as often as he attempted to go out, Pherenikos would twitch in his sleep and the Syracusan tyrant would freeze into immobility. Next to him, his jockey Chrysippos slept soundly.

Scarcely had dawn come when the stables were opened. The horses, led out of the dark, began neighing and tossing their heads upwards to the sky, as if they were invoking Helios, their patron. Men rushed out of their tents, half naked and only half awake. On the hard-baked earth the hoofs resounded with a metallic clatter like that of cymbals. The stately grace of the animals caused a delightful thrill. It seemed as if they had arrived from another world, that in their perfection of form they set before one's eyes the "idea", the supernatural model to which the common horse bears but a distant and blurred resemblance.

Among them there were offspring of myths, horses from the Argolid, from Attica, from Euboea. Their ancestors had been ridden by Hippolytos, the son of the Amazon; they had in their veins the blood of the marvellous mares of King Diomedes; in their history there had been occasions when from under their galloping hoofs springs had gushed out; and the sea-god Poseidon had taken the shape of a horse to impregnate Demeter. Their swiftness they owed to long ages of migrations and wars; their noble souls had learned faithfulness and sacrifice in the camps of the knights with whom they had passed away in the smoke of the burial pyre. Not a tendon, not a muscle that made up their admirable structure was the result of chance; on them had been lavished through generations the uninterrupted care of men who were of the same noble strain as they.

Not in the least inferior to these creatures were the horses of Sicily and Great Greece. Their pedigree was shorter, but they had been reared in the greatest luxury. The most improbable tales were told about the splendour of their stables, about doctors watching over their health, about the oats, barley and wheat measured out for them, about the music played when they mated so that the foals might be beautiful, and about the monuments that were erected in memory of them after their death. Some, charmed by their graceful forms, were positive that they were fed with flowers. As a matter of fact, the Kyrenaeans did give lotuses to their horses. They derived from a Libyan stock and were rusty red, like foxes. Their contours were characteristic: the back decidedly hollow, and above it the broad croup rising in an arch.

At sight of the Persian horses a murmur arose. Captured at the overthrow of the camp at Plataeae, they had already spread across the world through trade. Theron owned a whole team of four. Prisoners were brought as grooms to attend to them. Each had been promised freedom in the event of victory and death in case of defeat: no other way was seen whereby one could be sure of a vigilance over these animals whose habits and training nobody knew. But the horses moved about restlessly as if the scent of the strange nation were irritating to them. The Ionians from Asia Minor, the frequenters of divers roads, recognised among them the broad-chested horses of Cappadocia and pointed out those which came from Bithynia, Phrygia and Maeonia.

Not a single horse was black. Nobody dared to mount or harness to a carriage animals that by virtue of their colour belonged to the deities of death and the underworld. All shades of bay, roan, chestnut and grey moved about in beautiful contrast, among them a Nisaean pair most noticeable on account of their dazzling whiteness.

The horses were bathed in the sacred water of the Alpheios. The mounted grooms rode with them to midstream and after a dip or two returned to the bank. Here the horses were combed and one could see with one's own eyes the gold and silver combs which the Sicilian tyrants' men took out of leather bags. After that they were rubbed over with olive-oil, like human athletes. Their beautiful long manes were parted and combed down both sides and the forelock was curled. The manes of the Persian horses were clipped on the near side. The tails of those which were to be the side-horses of the team, were plaited and tied into a thick knot close to the rump.

Slaves brought water. They had been dispatched to distant hill springs during the night. Each of them was accompanied by a trustworthy person, who examined the vessel before it was filled with water, and later closed and sealed it. These seals were now tested and removed by the masters themselves. The big-bellied bronze receptacles contained a quantity of water that had been determined after prolonged consideration. Before it was given to the horses, a few goblets of wine would be poured in to stimulate the animals. They were all kept with empty stomachs, save those in the charge of the Persians, who fed their horses on a handful of lucerne.

The riders and drivers had finished their toilet. The former were naked and rubbed over with olive-oil like athletes, while the latter wore long white chitons which, tied at the waist, hung down to the ankles in parallel folds, like fluted columns. At the neck, where the chitons were cut away, could be seen the strings of the amulets which they wore on their bosoms. Their dangerous profession was steeped in superstitions that had come down the ages. One of them, in a frightened whisper, swore he would never again take part in the Isthmian Games.

"It seemed to me that a jet of steam had suddenly shot out from under the earth. It was not till I was carried off the course, chariot and all, that I heard that the son of Sisyphos, Glaukos, who met his death in the races, wanders there about the hippodrome."

At this the others shrugged their shoulders. The Isthmian Glaukos could be called a good spirit in comparison to the Olympian demon who haunts the eastern end of the hippodrome, where there is a post to indicate the spot for turning. Nobody knows his real name, they just call him Taraxippos—he who terrifies horses.

"He looks like a ghost with fiery glaring eyes!" "Like a child with an old face, a long beard and dishevelled hair!" "He is a bird!" "He creeps out suddenly, like a mole from under the earth, just beneath the horses' legs!" "He buzzes terribly like a monstrous horsefly!"

What he really looks like is not known. Most probably he can take on any form that suits his fancy, and more than one person has seen how he has changed into a horse and, as the fifth in the team, has run with the chariot, until he wrecked it. Seldom has any god had such zealous devotees. The whole night through offerings were placed on his altar. Drivers, riders and the masters in person heaped thereon a pile of flat cakes that had been fried in honey. They had thrown in their ribands, their wreaths, they had cut off a piece of their garments or even a lock of their hair, in order to give him some part of themselves in return for the safety of their horses and their own persons.

Striking the ground with their palms they would repeat: "Taraxippos, go into the field, go into the wood, go to the roads where carriages are driving." Or even: "Taraxippos, I have at Etna a stud of horses and I offer them to you for your pastime." They would suggest to him thousands of places which he ought to visit, they would offer him their stables, their byres, they thought out for him the wildest pranks to perpetrate in towns or mountain passes, they would even frankly scoff at him for living like an inert snail, always under the same post, when the whole world was before him, unexplored and full of interest. Others would threaten him with the wrath of the more powerful demons: "You will be tied up, Taraxippos, and burdened with a huge stone; you will suffer for a thousand years, until my offspring, whose name I do not know, shall liberate you with a countercharm."

But now the horses were harnessed to the chariots. The drivers were watching every movement of the grooms; they examined every part of the chariot, which was modelled on the war-chariots of old and, like them, had two high wheels, but was less broad, affording room for one person only in its light body, which was open at the back. The harness and reins glittered with gold. The masters handed the drivers the whips with a gesture so serious and full of dignity that it seemed the transfer of a province was being made. The riders wound leather straps round their legs down to the ankles. There were no stirrups or saddles. Seizing the mane, they leaped on to the horses' backs. Behind them followed the chariots.

Sotion awoke in a deserted barrack. Not only were the boys' beds empty, for they, being no longer contestants, had shifted over to the camp, but the men too had dashed off earlier.

The linen curtain at the entrance had been flung on to the roof, and in the rectangular opening a patch of the sky showed. The first ray of the sun appeared from behind the mountains and struck a white cloud, which turned a rosy pink, lasted for some moments, incomparably charming, and then dissolved into pale space: the burning lips of the day had quaffed in one gulp this rosy foam.

The young Tarentine, who was not in the habit of searching for signs in the sky, witnessed this circumstance and it impressed him, for he had presumed that this day could not start in the same way as all the others. By a common illusion he found himself in the centre of the cosmos.

He had plenty of time ahead of him. There were no other means of measuring it than by one's own shadow. Sotion, running out from the barracks, looked about for this huge accompanying shade which would later become shorter and shorter. When it started lengthening again, the time for the pentathlon would have arrived.

There was nobody to be seen between the barracks

and the Bouleuterion. All had gone to the riverside where the horses still were, or to the hippodrome, which had already begun to fill. Not far away, however, familiar voices could be heard. Sotion, following after them, entered the brushwood that overgrew the bank of the Kladeos. Down below, between high perpendicular walls of yellow sandstone, coursed a narrow streamlet. The competitors were washing themselves. They were standing in the water which reached up to their ankles. To scoop it up with their palms, they would bend down, and the curves of their bodies formed arches along the brook like the spans of a bridge. They took up whole handfuls of sand from the bottom and rubbed their skin with it, and great blotches of red appeared on their chests and backs.

They related their dreams and talked about omens.

Almost each one on his way to Elis had made a pilgrimage to some oracle or other. They discussed the perplexing words which they had received in answer from Apollo at Klaros, on Delos, at Ptoon, at Delphi; some had heard the murmur of the sacred oak in Dodona, the voice of Teiresias had foretold the future to another at Tilphusium on the Triton, and Gerenos subsequently disclosed that he had slept in the charmed cavern of Trophonios at Lebadea.

"To me the augury of the horses at Onchestos seems the surest," said Ladas. "It is carried out on the field in front of the grove of Poseidon. The horses are put to a chariot, whipped up and let loose without a driver. If they go straight into the grove, one can be certain of a win."

Pataikos and Epharmostos, who possessed nothing but

their own dreams and a few amulets, felt absolutely un-
shielded. Suddenly they heard Kallias, the descendant
of the Eleusian priests, saying:

"Here there is an oracle too. The soothsayers, whose
ancient ancestry goes back to Iamos and Klytios, inter-
pret dreams and know the meaning of any drift which
the smoke from a burnt offering takes. Olympia was an
oracle before it was the place of the Games."

At that moment Sotion jumped down. He landed just
behind Kallias.

"Which star have you fallen from?" smiled the
Athenian.

"From the moon."

"And what do they talk about there?"

"They say that to-morrow there will be a full moon."

"Ah! That is a prediction which may be relied upon,"
said Gryllos.

Sotion entered the water and showed what it means
to wash in an Olympic stream at dawn on the day of
one's own event. Under his soles a disturbance was
created, fountains spurted and, as if he had tapped new
springs, where the others had found a handful of water,
he splashed up whole waves. He whirled round in a frantic dance, he snorted, he shouted, and the water, which
he churned with his hands and feet, raved together with
him in an access of laughter. He rushed out of this bath
in a daze, with widely dilated eyes in which the world
still spun round through the eddying in the water, but
his blood was kindled and animated and a great glow
encompassed his body.

He got a comb from Gryllos in the same manner as
on his first day in Elis he had obtained the vessel of

olive-oil from him. He combed out his wet hair, and when he tossed it back a lighter patch of skin like a crescent of the moon appeared on his forehead. Gryllos assisted him to braid it in two plaits which he wound round his head, but he tied their ends together on his forehead and covered this with his fringe.

They were talking about yesterday's races. Eurymenes was praising Theognetos.

"Themistokles spoiled everything. Nobody followed that bout. It was really grand."

"And moreover," said Pataikos, "he defeated Drakon who is an Olympic victor. Such a win counts double."

"It would surely count for much," interrupted Gryllos, "if the last Olympiad had been worth anything. But there weren't even forty competitors at it."

All of a sudden Sotion became aware of Ikkos's absence. He could as well have noticed the absence of many others who had dispersed themselves about the camp, but he had sufficient cause to think specially of him. Where had he gone? The camp certainly did not attract him, he was not of those people who hover about among the tents and start conversations with those they meet. It was still less probable that he had gone to have a look at the horses or was searching for a seat in the hippodrome, for he had one, together with the other competitors, reserved near the tent of the hellanodikai.

Sotion walked along the Kladeos up to that spot at which the bank dips and affords an entrance to the Altis. From there he went straight to the stadium.

Ikkos was on the track. He was standing with his *halteres* still in his hands; his servitor was in the act of measuring the length of his leap. Bent over the spear, which served him as a measure, he turned his head on hearing a sound in the sand. He became confused as if he were caught in an evil act, and glanced at his master. Ikkos turned round too.

"Are you doing the whole pentathlon like that?" inquired Sotion.

"I should like to, if you'd keep me company in the wrestling."

"All right, but in the afternoon."

Meanwhile the attendant had measured the leap and whispered a number to Ikkos, who nodded.

"I take it you see something improper in this?" He turned again to Sotion.

"It does not depend on what I think about it, but if you are seen by any of the Council members or by one of hellanodikai. . . ."

"I know, and for that reason I chose a time when they are occupied with something else. I know these people. It will not occur to them till a hundred years hence to build a gymnasium and a palestra here."

"Then wait a hundred years, but meanwhile respect the custom which forbids the use of the Olympic stadium for practices."

Ikkos made a sign to his boy, who immediately removed everything.

"I hope you won't give me away?"

"Why are you suddenly afraid of me," said Sotion, astonished, "when you had the courage to come here, where anybody might see you?"

"Did you know that I was here?"

"I supposed so, and I came to warn you."

"By Zeus! It looks as if you were afraid to lose me."

Sotion kept silent, wondering at the oddity of this man. Ikkos, painstaking and cautious, thorough and far-seeing, on the very day of his event could expose himself to a risk which might end in a flogging or in exclusion, or both.

"I don't understand," he said, "why you do that."

"You don't understand? We left Elis on the tenth. To-day is the thirteenth. For the past five days I have not exercised. When I am with people like you, that is the sort of question I find I must answer. One would imagine I was talking to people who had never seen a gymnasium."

"And listening to you, one could conclude that you are a barbarian—one who does not know our customs. Surely you could have found another spot."

"I have entered for the pentathlon and not for goat-chasing. Would you have me run and jump on a stubble field?"

"Ergoteles has found a wonderful meadow at Harpina."

"At Harpina! Six stades there and six stades back. I suppose you would be glad if I returned with legs of lead?"

"Buy yourself a mule!"

And he left him at the Heraion. He had no patience with talk of this sort, which always ended in an undertone of contempt and hatred. No comprehension of any sort could exist between them. They belonged to two worlds strange to each other. Sotion's world was still so much in power that in it Ikkos figured somewhat like an irritating eccentric who is given a wide berth. And when Sotion passed through the open area in the east part of the Altis, he had for company the statues of men who represented all his ideals: bravery and strength obedient to the laws of Life, the glad submission to all regulations, health free of distrust and avarice. Their smiling faces looked towards the east, their bodies of wood, marble and bronze gleamed with the fresh sunlight and their shadows actually hid among the trees that grew behind them.

This very day could set him in their ranks. That thought brought him to a standstill. With one glance he took in this whole array of the famous, from the post of Oinomaos up to the Bouleuterion, and he noticed that he could find a place here. The statues were not yet closely packed, between them there was still plenty of vacant space, not even occupied by memorial tablets. But just as in a dream it is impossible to see one's own face, so Sotion could not imagine his own statue. He got no further than the plinth with his own name on it, higher up there was only a blank which he could not fill with any shape. He felt ashamed, eventually, at this vanity.

"Evidently," he reflected, "my marble still reposes under the earth!"

Ikkos, however, coming from the Heraion, passed the prytaneion and entered the wood which spread without a break up to the slopes of Mount Kronos. Here old plane-trees grew and under their dense crowns it was almost dark. The servitor, carrying the gymnastic equipment, lagged a few paces behind. Having lost sight of Ikkos in the shade of the trees, he started calling out to him. They were like two wanderers who had lost their way in some deserted region in the far west.

They say that during his lifetime man happens to

233

cross his grave, that with the sole of his foot he touches the site where he will meet his end and that this moment never passes by unnoticed, but announces itself by a sudden unexplained fear which would be felt quite clearly if at that moment the soul were free of all thoughts, of all impressions, tranquil and open like a blank space. Similarly our paths cross the roads of the future and occasionally we turn round as if at the sound of paces coming behind us. It may be that time, from the beginning of existence up to the end of all things, spreads out like a level plain. On this everyone traces out his own track, and if he were to swerve from it for a moment, he would immediately step either into what we call the past or into what is to come.

By the prytaneion Ikkos was treading the ground of the future.

The whole space, wild and overgrown like a pathless jungle, was one day to change into a gymnasium with porticoes, with a large training-field of a length equal to that of the stadium, with separate arenas for boxers and wrestlers, equipped with all that was necessary in order that bodies intended for the Games should not suffer a lapse during their preparation for the test. Everything that Ikkos found lacking was to be provided and even surpassed here. No part of his consciousness gave him any hint of this; on one occasion only, when touching the trunk of a tree, did he have the impression that his palm was stroking a stone column.

"I am tired," he thought, "tired or off my balance. In the most important moment of my life I have neither peace nor a place to myself. To-day I have already committed one rash act, and now my senses are deceiving me.

For the last few days I have had no idea in what condition my muscles are."

This was wearing him down terribly. The daily application of care to his body being interrupted, he found himself at a loss, like a mariner who cannot fix the position of his ship. Ikkos's art—his strength and skill—consisted of calculations; he wound up each day of his exercises with a record in which there remained for the morrow something to be finished or to be left out. From all these statistics he possessed now only the results of the last hurried days in Elis and the measure of to-day's leap, which was creditable, it is true, but, being a single incident, did not furnish anything to go on. Left merely with probabilities, Ikkos lost courage.

Stumbling over protruding roots and passing round bushes that barred his way, he was full of bitterness. The time in which he lived was splitting at the seams and there was no method of substituting for it a new self-designed pattern.

On the east side of the Altis, however, Sotion walked smoothly in the grooves of his epoch, not suspecting how very little of it remained. His whole existence was in the thoughts, feelings and ambitions of his period, which fitted him faultlessly and harmonised with him even as his body harmonised with his soul.

Just then he woke up to the fact that he was nude and started making for the barracks. But the noise of the races made him turn back. He would not have been a Tarentine if he had remained unimpressed by the sound of horses' hoofs. He ran up the barrow of Hippodameia, from which there was a view over the course.

The chariot races had already begun. Thirty of them

were engaged—ten dozen horses at a gallop. Three laps
had been covered uneventfully, it seemed the spectacle
was going to finish up in this splash of colours, this
dazzle and war. But it was only the quiet dawn of events
that never set without a sanguinary blaze.

Twenty laps were still to be done, since the full length
of the race totalled seventy-two stades. The horses became more and more fiery. The drivers bending over the
chariot boxes, which reached up to their hips, threw
their lashes aside. From their tense faces, from their
strained muscles, it was evident what effort was being
employed to prevent the eagerness of the horses from taking a free rein.

During the fifth lap the off-wheeler in the team of
Karneades from Kyrene broke loose. The driver, unable
to stop the chariot, drove on to the start and there he
remained.

"He has bitten through the reins," he said.

So Taraxippos has commenced his pranks! Those who
knew the habits of the demon predicted dreadful things.
The loose horse joined another team and then again ran
by itself, strayed about on the course, running in front of
the onrushing chariots, or again following behind them,
and this continued until at the starting-point itself they
succeeded in capturing it with a lasso.

The chariots tore along in a wild rush, obscured by
a thick cloud of dust. The reddish soil under the sand
of the ploughed-up ground was laid bare, bruised
by the horses' hoofs, which were scattering lumps of
earth on the spectators in the front rows. The hippodrome narrowed, it became a whirling ellipse; the intoxicated souls of the people merged into the weird circle

of movement. The world, set aglow by the early heat, was near to boiling-point, the vault of the sky quivered like the lid of a pot.

And suddenly the spinning hoop burst.

The Argive chariot fouled the post marking the laps. The crash of broken wheels was followed by the shout of thousands of people. The Argive's horses swerved sideways and stumbled against the horses of Messana, which were the nearest. Confusion ensued; the oncoming chariots, unable to check their impetus, swooped upon each other like stars flung out of their orbit. They became involved in a monstrous tangle which only death could unravel.

But Theron's driver, who was at the tail end, succeeded in getting his horses under control in time. Approaching cautiously, he made a wide turn, avoiding this huge heap of chariots, animals and men, that resembled a throbbing volcano. He closed his eyes in order not to see anything, but the appalling picture forced its way to his brain through his ears, a hideous racket of squeals and moans.

The Olympian attendants ran out to give aid. The horses that had broken loose were caught, bodies that crumpled up when lifted, bodies rendered insensible and pale as death, were carried away; after they had gone, spots of blood remained on the sand. When Theron's team approached again, everybody dispersed to make way for it. And this chariot, the only one saved, coursed round the hippodrome unobstructed and without rivals.

The driver stood upright holding the reins high. As often as he approached the fatal post the spectators would

lapse into silence as they thought that Taraxippos would
not spare this victim too. Indeed, at the moment when
the herald's trumpet announced the last lap, the horses
from Akragas recoiled at the sight of their comrade's
corpse, which was lying there as yet unremoved. But the
driver subdued them and overcame their fear by re-
doubling their speed. They dashed round the empty
track as though fleeing before an unseen pursuer, until
they were liberated by the piercing blast of the trumpets
—at the empty goal.

Sotion descended from the barrow of Hippodameia.
Passing the tent of the hellanodikai, he heard someone
call. Aipytos beckoned to him with his hand.

"Have you seen Ikkos?" he inquired.

"Yes."

"Where?"

"Near the Heraion."

"But was he on the stadium?"

"I don't know."

"And whose are those tracks that have remained
there?"

"I know nothing about tracks. As for Ikkos, when I
met him he was coming from the prytaneion."

The hellanodikes nodded doubtfully:

"The kleiduchos saw one of the competitors busy
about the stadium. He says it must have been one of the
pentathletes."

"By Zeus! I can't imagine a kleiduchos knowing
what competitors go in for."

"He says that one had *halteres*."

"I did not see anything," said Sotion firmly.

"You may go. But if it is found out, you will be punished too."

Already the competitors knew all about it. They crowded round Sotion and began questioning him. He felt that if he started to answer their questions it would not be easy to elude them.

"You know," he whispered, "in the middle of the night Ikkos went to the stadium and there he did the whole pentathlon. As he had no partner to wrestle with, he asked Hermes. But don't tell anybody about that."

The joke appeased them. A thing that can be laughed over lost its gravity in their light souls, it became transported, as it were, to a planet of different mass.

"Let's go to the camp for a snack," said Sodamos; "later there won't be any time."

"My father's tent is the nearest," intimated Eutelidas.

It was empty, but at the Spartan's voice a helot came running up. He brought cheese, bread and fresh pears.

"Does it not seem to you," said Sodamos, "that the time we spent in Elis is already remote?"

What he really meant was: "This is our last breakfast together and shall we ever meet after the Games are over?" And this too: "Do say, wasn't the time in the gymnasium the most delightful, did it not comprise that which has the greatest value in life: a definite purpose?"

Each of them, of course (how could it be otherwise?) felt resting on his head the wreath which should transform him into quite another being, and this other being had no place amidst his former comrades; he remained outside the gate. In spite of its boundless renown, the achieved purpose desolated the heart which had lived so gloriously. Would a new aim equally divine ever present

itself? Would days of such glowing hope be met with
hereafter? Could the world replace by anything else the
inexhaustible charm of association and friendship which
had daily improved with noble emulation?

And unexpectedly a talk began in which the Games
did not figure at all, nor the anxiety preceding the decisive moment; all three entered into noisy reminiscences
of the gymnasium. From there they extracted names
connected with insignificant but unforgotten incidents,
they remembered the comrades who had failed to reach
Olympia, like men who perish in the last encounter before the proclamation of a truce.

The hippodrome was passing through its greatest
moments. After the race of the four-horse chariots there
followed the mule-drawn chariots. They were just six,
and all of them Sicilian. In Old Greece, Thessaly alone
possessed beautiful racing mules, but this year Thessaly
was not participating in the Games. The Eleans, whom
an age-old superstition had kept from breeding these
animals, had no liking for this contest. The chariot of
Anaxilas of Rhegion won.

Now they were just finishing the kalpe, the mares'
race.

Half-way through the last lap the riders, holding on
to the bridles, leapt to the ground. Carried onwards by
their impetus, they ran together with their mounts to
the goal. In this one event of the races the kings did not
participate. The minor gentry competed in the kalpe;
each one was the rider of his own mare with which he
had grown familiar from the time it was a foal. The
spectators, realising how little pomp and vanity there
was here and how much affection and skill, followed the

riders with an uninterrupted round of loud encouragement. The young Athenian, Kallippos, from the environs of Marathon, was the winner, on the mare Melissa. His race was worthy of the stadium.

But the kings came on the scene again when the race for riding-horses was proclaimed by trumpet. For more than one of them this was the second hazard of this day, after the calamity of the chariots. Among these was Hieron.

He had lost two horses which emerged with broken legs, and his driver was fatally injured. He suffered, however, not so much because of his own defeat, but because of the victory of Theron who, he suspected, had used charms. The thought that Theron would depart with a wreath, while he returned with empty hands, filled him with horror.

"Go," he said to Chromios, "and tell Chrysippos that he will receive a mina of silver if he wins."

"He will get two, for I will give him the second."

Chrysippos mounted the bay steed in such high spirits that it seemed he was already carrying those two minae in a bundle on his shoulders. Many knew the horse from the Pythian Games, and shouts of "Pherenikos!" were heard, which Hieron took as a good sign. He did not hear that the other horses were hailed in the same manner; from all sides there resounded: "Knakias!" "Phoinix!" "Aiolos!" "Phoibos!"

Pherenikos forged ahead, but in the next instant Phoinix outstripped him. This was repeated several times over the whole length of the hippodrome. Hieron had a feeling that he stood not on solid ground but on an agitated sea: now he was being lifted on the crest of a wave and then tossed down again. His weak kidneys were gripped as in a burning vice. It was death, this darkness that enveloped him each time Pherenikos lagged behind the red shape of Phoinix; it was new life, every time the light bay steed flew out into unobstructed space.

How irksome it is to be a king! Let anybody detach his eyes for a moment from the hippodrome and glance at this face of mortal dread, at its anguished burning blotches—it is awful not to be able to hide one's face which can mask nothing.

Once more he is tossed into gloomy depths. At the sight of the red head which thrusts itself to the fore, he closes his eyes and sinks into the endless dusk, and when the outcry: Pherenikos! raises him to life, Hieron, the sovereign of Syracuse, stands under the cruel firmament of thousands of eyes, pale, with livid lips and a forehead bathed in sweat.

Chrysippos has jumped down from the horse and is leading it, holding the bridle. He halts before Hieron, who with trembling hands ties round his brows the white ribbon of victory. Together they proceed to the tent of the hellanodikai. The rider remains a pace in the rear while Hieron, holding Pherenikos by his bright mane, waits until Kapros arranges the wreath of olive sprigs.

The herald, proclaiming the victory of the Syracusan horse, exerted himself in vain. Nobody listened to him any more, the crowd was already pouring out of the hippodrome and surging towards the stadium.

The sun was nearing its zenith, only a short time was allowed for the interval. At former Olympiads this was prolonged considerably, for the old hellanodikai, banqueting in kingly style, did not hurry over their dinner. But Kapros had prescribed but a short meal, which was already waiting in the prytaneion. Those who went to their tents took the risk of being late: half the treasuries were empty.

On the steps of one of them sat Themistokles. The people's throats, not yet sufficiently rested after the bawling in the hippodrome, disregarded these four beautiful syllables. Their voices were being reserved for new people, the champions of yesterday and to-day. Glaukos, Agesidamos, Theognetos and Kallippos were present, with white ribbons round their heads. Theron's driver, who had not discarded his long robe, and dust-covered sandals, brought news of the injured and related it at the top of his voice beneath the silent heights.

Others were busy eating. They had stores in their bundles, which they now unpacked, and frequently there would be bursts of laughter at the sight of the pulpy mass which their cheese, bread and fruit had become through the heat and the crowding.

So also appeared the track over which thousands of feet had passed. Who would search for Ikkos's incriminating footprints on it? They were forgotten, they had been strewn over with sand, fresh yellow sand, so clean and small-grained that it seemed it had been put through a sieve. Under the Olympian workmen's spades and rakes the stadium rolled out immaculate, creaseless and inviting, like a scroll of parchment that has not yet been marked by so much as a word but is ready to receive the full beauty and elevation of human inspiration.

The competitors' entry sounded, indeed, like the beginning of a poem in whose score or so of wondrous verses there is contained a presaging of strange and disquiet events, of fervour and the vagaries of fate, of reverses and triumphs, a poem which in its invocation addresses present deity.

The pentathlon produced the best-built men, the cream of pentathletes. The ceremony with the table and wreath was wearisome; princes arrived late on the scene, but no one paid any attention to them, the whole hillside in fixed silence was gazing at the competitors.

The eye, devouring these figures, moulded by an art that was beyond the capabilities of any sculptor then living, perceived more than could actually be taken in by one sense; it gratified, at the same time, touch, taste and smell, as if those forms were fruit with an indescribably delicate skin, a juicy pulp and an exquisite redolence. The competitors could have stood as they were till the evening and then departed, and nobody would have clamoured for the Games to continue; their mere presence would have been sufficient, as in certain festivals where a procession of perfectly built men ends the worship like a final prayer.

The sight of these bodies was comparable to everything that gives the quintessence of joy. It could be compared with a starry night, for in addition to their palpable sensual splendour there was in them the deep meaning that attaches to perfect things. They slaked the thirst for order as does the cosmos, but in a manner incalculably more intimate and warm-hearted, because they were, after all, the fruits of the earth, these fascinating beings, and the perfection they displayed did not transcend human possibility, but mingled with it, offering encouragement and at the same time a challenge.

The glances, straying from one competitor to the other, would return to Sotion, to remain fixed on him.

His physique, the rounded shapeliness of his head and neck, the delicate lips, the straight nose, the hair which in the sun appeared to be still lighter, the expressive eyes—the whole was of the purest Hellenic blood; the very soul of the race, it seemed, had embodied itself in this youth. He was admired as if the very landscape of the Fatherland were on view.

The pentathlon commenced with the ordinary flat race, the distance being one stade. The heats were run off with pairs. The eleven contestants were divided into four pairs and one trio. Sotion found himself in the last group, together with the two Arcadians. His was the last heat. Before him, Sodamos, Ischomachos, Eutelidas and Ikkos had won their respective heats.

Sotion's first stride from the start was so long that it seemed as if he had bounded. He occupied the centre position and, forging ahead from the very beginning, became the apex of a triangle, its other two angles moving always at the same distance behind him. About twenty feet before the goal one of the Arcadians darted forward with a spurt that painfully contorted his mouth. But at that instant Sotion, having finished the run, spread his arms out in a last movement and the Arcadian was checked at this living barrier.

A cheer greeted him. It was as fervent as if he were the only victor and this were already the finish of the pentathlon.

Sotion experienced a feeling which he could not fathom. For the first time in his life he was hearing the voice of the world. Hitherto, his youth had passed as quietly as if spent in a hermitage. True, he had lived in a continual stir, in an uninterrupted bustle, but the activity was of his own making and the noise was the resonance of his own blood coursing in his veins. The world, the people—he knew nothing about them, he thought of them in short sudden snatches, even as an arrow might have thought when flying over fields, houses and their occupants.

And suddenly that unknown world hailed him by name! It voiced his name distinctly, with all its three syllables, which had never until now seemed so precious and so dear. Ten, twenty, thirty thousand people reiterated this specific sound. How passionately and with what vigour! He had life in each of those voices that rent the air, he had being in each of those people, they were multiplying him by their untold numbers, and Sotion felt himself magnified beyond the bounds of imagination. Joy, causing a tremble as of fear, suffused his soul. Into it he peered with amazement: it was resplendent and ablaze as if the sun had risen in it.

A flute began to sound. It was played, not by a slave as in the gymnasium, but by laurel-wreathed Midas, the famous musician. To play at the pentathlon in Olympia was an honour, it was a distinction, for nobody could entertain hopes of a vaster audience. In the Altis, amidst the competitors, stood the statue of Pythokritos, who for a series of Olympiads had accompanied the competitors with his artistic music.

Prior to the melody usual at the Games, Midas piped the short composition that had been awarded the prize at Delphi. It was a prayer to Apollo. The faint note of the low-pitched aulos was unable to penetrate through the hum of the populace. It was only when silence prevailed that it ascended and straightened out like the sky-blue smoke-column from burning sacrificial incense.

Ischomachos began the jumps. He was good, but below his usual standard. The next marks went beyond his like the rungs of a ladder. On the topmost rung Sodamos settled, two finger-breadths ahead of Ikkos. Sotion, who leaped last, reached the same distance, covering with his feet the still fresh imprint of his friend.

The gracefulness of his leap was noticed by all. The eyes of the spectators, among whom any person unfamiliar with gymnastics would have been a unique exception, observed, picked out and committed to memory the least, most inappreciable movement. Had Sotion leaped two feet shorter than he did, the rapture would have been no less. This live dart, flying along an inimitable arch, demonstrated an excellence above all esteem. The Tarentine's body, knit to a run of notes of the music, seemed to be its sensuous symbol. And it was thus that Sotion's leap struck the spectators, in whose memory it remained as the fragment of a melody.

. . . .

It was always a solemn moment when the competitors were given their choice of the three discs which were brought from the treasury of the temple of Hera.

These were of the same size and weight and undoubtedly as ancient as the discus on which the sacred truce of the Games was engraved; they recalled the Age of Bronze or that sombre dawn of the Iron Age when the old Dynasty of Copper and Zinc, that had survived eons, that had reared up thousands of generations taken over from the Epoch of Stone, made way for the new world arising out of blood and fire. Time, however, had not deposited even the slightest trace of patina on them. Stored in leather bags and wrapped in cloth soaked in olive-oil, they would appear for a short spell once in four years, as though they had been awakened out of a long sleep. Their dull sheen reminded one of a serpent that spring has induced to shed its old skin. The competitors, taking them in their hands, saw in their smooth surface their own faces and could not master their emotions at the thought that perhaps a phantom or a spirit, conjured centuries ago into the metal, was looking at them.

With the exception of Ikkos, no one had any success with the first throw. The arrow marking his throw was almost twenty feet beyond those of the others which, embedded in different parts of the track, described a curve, indicating faulty balance.

Poor Ischomachos failed ignominiously. Three times his throw was disqualified because he stepped beyond the balbis boundaries. He stood now, his eyes swollen with tears, shattered and numbed. He had been banned from competing further.

"You may go and get dressed," shouted Hysmon.

Instinctively he looked at the nude body that was his pride, but it appeared to him to be of no use henceforth for the rest of his life.

All this was happening outside Sotion's sphere of consciousness. The crucial event had gripped him and had made him insensible to external impressions. Of all that world, the world which a few moments ago had called to him with its mighty voice, there remained only a single slip, the slender crimson-feathered arrow marking Ikkos's throw. A while later it was joined by another, almost on the same spot: Ikkos worked with balance and precision.

Sotion, awaiting his turn, could not keep still. Impatience, like love-longing, was exhausting him. At last he snatched the discus with his sweaty palm and, without strewing sand over it, he hurled it. Its circle twisted in the air and was still spinning like a top on the stadium, yet the spot at which it first touched the ground was but a sad notch amongst the worst throws.

It was then that the public showed Sotion its heart. Everybody felt as he did, and understood; the souls nurtured in the gymnasiums and attuned to an emulatory instinct clearly discerned what was taking place within him. He was like a somnambulist, and the slightest sound might hurl him over the precipice. Not a single murmur was heard.

But it was for reasons quite otherwise that the spectators held their breath when Sotion for the third time approached the balbis.

He was now quite composed. He thrust the right leg forward and, though the weight of the body was supported on the left leg, the right, with its tense calf muscles, and the firmly planted foot were ready to uphold him in his action. He resorted to it next moment, when passing the discus from the left to the right hand. He bent forwards and then sharply turned to the right—his whole frame twisted, a living pre-figuration of Myron's bronze —and straightened up again, shifting the weight of the body on to the left leg. Then, for the last time, he stepped back; his arm made three swings like a pendulum—a grand lever of tendons and muscle—and, finally, discharged the discus.

It flew level, cutting the air noiselessly, one could have taken it for a streak of fire, and when it descended it bounced up with a ring—once, twice, thus in a mortal paroxysm parting with its soul, its content of eternal motion.

After the throw Sotion remained with arms outspread and poised upon the muscles of his right leg. His lungs were full of breath, until a sonorous impulsive shout burst from them when the discus passed Ikkos's mark.

After the javelin throwing a conference was held between the hellanodikai. The results of the four events of the pentathlon were discussed in order to determine who was to line up for the wrestling, the deciding item.

"I don't know if this is necessary," said Hysmon. "The winner in three events can be taken as the winner of the whole pentathlon."

"Yes," retorted Aipytos, "but Sotion is not the proved winner."

"Why? Because the Arcadian threw the javelin better?"

"No. The Arcadian does not count at all."

"Then who does?"

"Ikkos, Sodamos."

"Sodamos has leaped the same distance as Sotion," Onomastos pointed out, "but who would think of comparing him with Sotion? Moreover, a measure is not the deciding factor with us. Let each one ask himself who is the best of them all, who has the greatest worth not for that single moment of the Games, the moment of hasty chance, but for every occasion when man has recourse to his strength and skill."

"Sodamos cannot be rejected," objected Aipytos, "and that for the very same reasons."

"By Zeus!" said one of the guardians of the law. "Sodamos cannot be rejected, but still our Olympic custom adds this too: If there are three worthy, brave and honest contestants in the pentathlon, none of them should be conceded the turn of sitting by."

The "sitter by" (*ephedros*) was that one of three whom the casting of lots reserved for the end, for a bout with a tired opponent. Yesterday that lot had fallen to Pytheas and made his defeat doubly lamentable. Actually, none of the victors of the pentathlon deserved this. Kapros settled the matter by including Eutelidas.

"He deserves it," he said, "as a worthy competitor, as a Spartan, and out of respect for the name he bears."

But this name was to be reputed no more in the annals of Olympian victors.

Eutelidas could not cope with Ikkos whom chance had pitted against him. He went down quicker even than was expected, almost too quickly for the eye to follow, since the full attention of the spectators was concentrated on the other pair. The bouts were simultaneous because Kapros did not wish the Games to drag on till dusk.

Ikkos, having got rid of his opponent, had time not only to rest, to fulfil all the ceremonies of cleansing and refreshing the skin, but also to study the bout between Sotion and Sodamos. He followed it intently and kept in mind a vast number of important and useful details. After a while he gave up watching Sodamos, as it was evident that he would have to deal with Sotion.

He did not have to wait long for him. Here he came in a hurricane of cheering, dripping with sweat, like a god begotten of clouds and lightnings.

In the enclosure reserved for the trainers, he had his vessel of olive-oil. One handed him a towel, another massaged his back. As though spirits were serving him, he did not utter a word, he could not tell one face from another. When his body was dry, he rubbed olive-oil into it.

The empty aryballos slipped from his fingers. Sotion kicked it away as a useless thing. The small round vessel went rolling down the steps of the terrace. Hydna, sitting in the front row, bent down, lifted it and held it in her palm. Her eyes met Sotion's glance. The girl's noble look expressed admiration, esteem and confidence, and was as hearty as the strong embrace of a comrade.

From the very first holds Sotion perceived that he had to deal with a new, unknown Ikkos. The whole "void" which had startled them all so much in the gymnasium instantly filled up. There Ikkos had only defended himself; here he was leading the attack. Sotion, taken quite by surprise, succumbed to the opening manœuvre which he was unable to foresee. The hand with which he tried to prop himself sank deep into the sand and touched the very earth. This strengthens and gives life anew, for in man's veins flows the blood of Earth's sons, the Giants.

Sotion felt it in himself. It responded with a kindling fire, with a flame of wrath and anger. Had he at that moment possessed the use of Gerenos's muscles, he would have choked this man of secret ways. This was no longer Ikkos, the friend of former years; neither was he an object of dislike nor a bone of contention to avoid—this was a hostile force, rapacious and cruel. More than his own victory he desired his adversary's defeat.

For the moment he could do nothing else but remain on guard, and even this was not easy. Open through and through on all occasions, he had given his whole self in every encounter, and during those months, while they had been together in Elis, Ikkos had been able to observe him thoroughly. Indeed, he knew him by heart. His first move, even the hint of a move, at times the flash of the eyes—those beautiful bright frank eyes—sufficed to enable Ikkos to frustrate his tactics. There were no un-solved problems in him. Ikkos read him like a child's school-task.

What, however, did keep him in check was Sotion's inexhaustible freshness. Each time he attempted some decisive hold, putting the whole store of his strength into it, he would meet with a resistance so alert and resolute that he himself would not have been capable of it, had Sotion relinquished his defence for other tactics. The latter, however, remembered only too well his first fall, which had been so sudden and unexpected. He relied now only on the elasticity of his body. Ikkos went through strained moments of ineffectual effort, as if he were wrestling with a waterspout.

But he soon weighed the situation. He was now more sparing with his movements and less eager to engage. He gradually got his opponent used to the thought that he was no more fit for anything but defence. Once or twice he reeled slightly, as if unsteady on his legs. Sotion thought this weakness real. With a naively frank gesture he made as if to grasp Ikkos's neck but instantly bent down to catch his leg and toss him over. Ikkos stepped back one pace; Sotion lost his balance and fell.

It cannot be said that he was up in a trice. He took some time and did not straighten at once but remained on all fours, with knees and both hands in the sand. Then, before he resumed the opening stance, he wiped his perspiring face; his hand, soiled with dust, left absurd ugly smears. Dusty patches covered his knees, on his hips and chest blotches showed, and one calf was hidden behind a greave of sand. He looked like a man in rags.

The cordial alliance which a large group of the spectators had made with him on the stadium was broken. The first to forsake him were the Tarentines. With two competitors from Tarentum to choose from, they finally selected the one who gave them a greater assurance of victory. When voices were raised on behalf of Ikkos, nobody supported them at the start; here and there some even shouted Sotion's name. But these were no longer wings that could soar high. They flapped more and more hesitant, they grew weak.

In one afternoon Sotion acquired the experience of a long life. The world, which he did not know and for which he had not cared, had lured him, had saturated him with the pleasure of its idolatry, allowed him to feel all the charms of its proximity and its applause, and when it seemed to him that the greatest hardship would be to find oneself beyond its horizon, it turned away from him, and Sotion was left forsaken to drain to the very dregs, in a single moment that was as full as years, the bitter lesson of loneliness.

Unexpectedly the figure of Sodamos loomed up in

his troubled soul. He saw him as he had held him, a short while back, in his firm grasp: the hair dishevelled, the face flushed and bathed in sweat, with pale streaks of fatigue on it, but the eyes peering forth with the unshaken calm of Heracles's devotees.

The image was momentary as a flash of lightning, and equally dazzling. Sotion, to whom the bout gave no opportunity for thought, depriving him, in fact, of all consciousness, perceived subconsciously the full significance of the vision and, as if harkening to a voice in a prophetic dream, awoke with a smile. He was his real self again, a zealous and jubilant competitor, officiating in the body's magnificent liturgy.

But his sacrifice was approaching its end. Exhausted by his vigorous forenoon, his expense of energy in the contests, his struggle with Sodamos, he was unable to cope with his frugal antagonist. Ikkos was subsisting on what he had conserved during the course of the day; on what might be expressed thus: light training in the morning, plus massage, plus sleep before dinner in the pines' shade on the slopes of Kronion. Add the small scraps gathered during the competitions, crumbs of energy not frittered away on any superfluous movement, and finally, the combat with Eutelidas, easy and short, allowing time for more rest.

All that taken together was at the moment a great asset in comparison with the resources of Sotion, who possessed nothing whatever.

For the last time he bounded forward to engage, raising his hands to seize Ikkos; but the latter caught him round the waist and grappled him with a stranglehold while his hands, still outstretched, remained upraised as if they were supporting an invisible bowl. Sotion, breathless, with a smile which appeared to be escaping like a spirit from his pallid face, rose upwards automatically, as if with trembling lips he was forced to quaff the last wine of his improvident festive revelry. Now his feet no longer touched earth; Ikkos cut it away from under them, he snatched the earth from him, and Sotion, as a defaulter deprived of his house sinks down on his creditor's doorstep, collapsed while the last beams of the sun strewed on him their useless gold.

CHAPTER VII

THE FESTIVAL OF FULL MOON

THE Greek day was reckoned from evening to evening. The finish of the pentathlon closed the fourteenth day of the month of Parthenios, and the new day was born in the amber hues of the sunset.

It was a festive day, a fitting celebration for the full moon. In times gone by this one revolution of the earth round its axis comprised in its compass of light and darkness the entire festival, the offering and the Games. But the Games had developed, and the ever-increasing number of competitors could not be fitted into a single day, which in the end broke up like a sun, and surrounded itself with four planets. It remained, of course, not only the pivot, but also the source of everything. From it, from its essentials, filled with prayer and sacrificial smoke, the Games had waxed in importance; they, as a separate unit, had become a part of the cult, and the stadium led to the altar of Zeus like a pilgrim path.

That day had two halves, a dark and a light one. The latter, beginning at daybreak, started the moiety of Zeus and the heavenly deities, whereas nightfall ushered in the season of the spirits, demons and subterranean gods.

The first to come forward were the sacrificers with offerings for Pelops. On the barrow of the hero a fire was lit and a black ram was slaughtered. The Xyleus, the wood-cutter of the sacred grove, cut off a portion of the flesh from the neck and placed it apart. This was his right—an unusual one, for nobody was permitted to touch or to eat the flesh of animals that were sacrificed to the powers below. The blood of the beasts belongs to the earth in which ghosts dwell, and the black ram's blood drained into a hole which led to the interior of the barrow. The flesh, bones and skin of the animals were to be digested by the undying fire, and so the black ram burned on the altar which was heaped continually with fresh firewood until all had turned into ashes and charcoal.

This lasted long. The moon had already emerged from behind the mountains of Triphylia, but the sacrificers, gazing steadfastly into the fire, waited. At last one of them started invoking Pelops. He summoned his soul, that had had its fill of the fresh blood, and recounted to it the events at Olympia where, once upon a time, the hero had ruled; he invited him to visit the Games.

Meanwhile the Iamidai, the Olympic soothsayers, had gathered in a small round chapel which stood behind the sacred grove. The chapel was empty and dark. The officiators took with them torches, the thick pitchy smoke of which ascended in columns under the timber-work of the roof. By the southern wall was a low hearth, the eschara, an ordinary stone block hewn into a regular shape. On it, with his flambeau, the eldest of the Iamids set fire to a handful of brushwood and strewed incense into the flames. "Iamos! Iamos!"—the Olympic soothsayers were addressing their ancestor, the son of Apollo. They sang a hymn.

The narrow interior of the chapel became charged with smoke from the hearth and from the torches; the air grew thick and stifling. People choked and coughed, tears welled up in their eyes. The beautiful old verses of the hymn died away in their phlegm-laden voices, in them wilted the violets that were mentioned in it, the violets that grew at the river's edge on which the virgin Euadne had laid her child. The whole life of Iamos, interwoven with sunbeams and flowers, crumbled and disintegrated like a withered stalk in the confused gurgling of these voices. Of all that in bygone days this son of a god had been there remained in the end only ashes and smoke; the flambeaux died out, the round chapel took on the appearance of a grave; a dusk spread through it, the dusk of death, which even the gods are unable to escape.

And in such wise, on this evening drenched in the full moon's light, in the vicinity of the camp, where fires gleamed and a clamour rang out, the sacrificers hovered around the dead demigods at the barrow of Endymion that lay under the hill of Kronos and at the grave of Oinomaos beyond the Kladeos. Thence they repaired to the neighbourhood of Harpina where under a common mound lay the wooers of Hippodameia. They invoked all thirteen of them, in the same order in which they had perished long ago under the lance of the king of Pisa: Mermos, Hippothoos, Pelops of Opus, Akarnan, Eurymachos, Eurylochos, Automedon, Lasios, Chalkon, Trikoronos, Alkathoos, Aristomachos and Krokalos. At the boundaries of Heraea others called Koroibos, the first victor at the Olympic Games, to come forth from the grave. And in Elis, far away, the priestesses, grouped around the cenotaph of Achilles, were weeping and beating their bosoms, as if he had only just died, and later with joyous shouts they besought him to come to the Games, where he ought to be—he, eternally coeval with competitors.

On this night scarcely anybody in the camp slept. There was too much to do in connection with the morning sacrifices. People washed, combed and dressed their hair and beards; the slaves were running for water, cleaning and pressing out chitons and chamydes, and braiding wreaths; sacrificial animals were being carefully tended; people were consulting each other about taking part in the processions; the lack of something essential would suddenly be noticed, a rush would be made to booths that had closed, and vendors would be sought out among the tents. The full moon shone on this bustle and marked the time of the waning night by her passage.

Before dawn the hearths burned out and the tents began to quieten down. Between the wall of the Atlis and the Kladeos there were swarming groups whose white garments merged into the mist that spread over the valley. More and more were joining them; in the semi-darkness the dull hum of the crowd reverberated gradually, the unshapely mass narrowed and lengthened, as if invisible hands were moulding it. What was happening was that the members of the Olympian Council were allocating positions in the state procession. Their voices, already grown hoarse, were contending with the irritability of man, which every now and then would engulf them by a louder and more vehement clamour. The sections, after being linked together with much trouble, would break loose again; it seemed this was never going to end. But from those that had meantime got ready for the road came the cry: "Dawn! Dawn!" and this magic word, announcing the most sacred part of the day, promptly soothed all. The column began to move, orderly and peacefully, under the brightening sky, as if there had arisen from the shadows, from the dusky chaos, a new human species.

Passing along the western wall of the Altis, the column came to a standstill when the Olympian Council, in the van, met with the college of the hellanodikai. This purple link united the state processions with the equally white retinues of the priests who were waiting at the prytaneion. These now proceeded at the head of the column along the usual processional way, which led between the temple of Hera and the barrow of Pelops.

In the first row were the three theokoloi, the supreme priests of the Olympic cult; behind them, carrying golden chalices, were the spondophorae with the long staffs of divine heralds; the kathemerothytes, the priest who performed the daily sacrifice on the altar of Zeus, although he had to-day entrusted his duties to one of the theokoloi, went with them himself in order to see that the ceremonies were properly carried out. He was accompanied by two exegetes, masters of ritual each with a papyrus scroll containing the sacrificial procedure. Their hoary heads, however, retained more than the papyri did, for they had treasured up an inexhaustible store of tradition from the time when Zeus had assumed command over Olympia.

But these seemed mere youths in comparison with what was represented by those who came behind them, the

Basilai. As Kronos, their god, who had grown out of the
chaos of a world only just born and still retaining its
original molten state, himself hidden in the darkness of
eternal night, so they belonged to epochs equally far and
dark, when the ages, like mountains thrown up by the
spasms of the earth, had waxed and waned in the dim
break of day under the red streak of dawn. Then, while
wandering tribes overran the lands of Greece, some in-
cidental surge had brought this god and set him on these
ranges, and prayers were offered up to him with human
blood at the time of the spring equinox. The Basilai were
but the remnant of a time-worn cult. Thrust aside together with their god, they walked in the retinue of his
successor, passive and subordinate, like the descendants
of a conquered nation.

Grouped in the succeeding rows were the Olympic
soothsayers, the kleiduchi who had charge of the
temples and treasuries, the xyleus, the spondauloi with
their flutes, and some tall and powerful assistants of the
priests with their axes for slaughtering the animals. The
priests' servitors carried baskets containing implements
for the sacrifices, large copper kettles and slim hydrias
of water. The victims themselves were led along in the
rear—bulls and rams, all of them pure white. This was
the Elean hecatomb, and tithes of stock collected from all
the herds in the country. Their horns gilded and be-
decked with garlands of flowers and leaves, they walked
quietly and half drowsily, stupefied by the infusion of
poppy-seeds which had been mixed with their last
meal.

The retinue of priests halted before the altar; the
hellanodikai together with the Olympic Council seated

themselves on the steps of the terrace. Between the altar and the terrace was a free space for the state processions.

Each of these was led by an architheoros and a proxenos accompanied by high dignitaries and eminent citizens; amongst the Athenians was Themistokles, among the Spartans marched the ephors, everywhere one saw men and boys with wreaths on their brows. These were the victors from Olympia, Delphi, Nemea and the Isthmus, the living ornaments of each contingent; every country strove to exhibit as many as it could, even wizened veterans who had distinguished themselves on the stadium in years gone by were not left out. This year fresh wreaths made the processions of Chios, of Lokri, and of Ægina illustrious; Ikkos paced at the head of Tarentum in princely eminence.

And the same spirit of rivalry encumbered the processions with loads of sacrificial implements, vessels of silver and gold by means of which the wealth of their countries was expressed. Hundreds of hands carried innumerable identical kraters, bowls, cups, thymiateria exuding the smoke of fragrant incense; there were parties so loaded that it seemed they were returning from a distribution of the spoils of war. These were the representatives of states which possessed their own treasuries at Olympia. They had taken out everything that their ancestors had collected: gold wreaths, horns of plenty, relics of heroes, chests and caskets, statuettes of gods and, lastly, objects, fossils from other ages, that had no name nor any indication of their use. These things were carried as emblems of the fatherland, to symbolise its live and tangible presence, that by means of some visible bond each could cleave to his own bit of territory and not be swamped in this white flood which was uninterruptedly pouring out from the processional road.

The column stretched out indefinitely. It included numberless states and colonies; if all were not there, those that were absent belonged either to the remote parts or, though near, were hidden in wild mountainous regions among barbarous customs. All the more conspicuous was the absence of Thessaly, the ally of the Persians, and the gap could almost be felt in that place between Sparta and Syracuse where princes of the Aleuad line once had proudly walked, always bringing with them a full hecatomb of a hundred bulls. Neither was Thebes there, but, as a special privilege, her place was occupied by Pindar. He was alone, with only a servitor behind him, leading two rams.

The processions passed by the altar and arranged themselves on the stadium. The priests were waiting until all should muster, gazing every few moments at the eastern sky, which had begun to glow like gold. The low hillock of Pisa could not hold back the sun for long. It burst forth suddenly in dazzling brilliance from behind there; its rays spread over the multitude and were reflected in the glittering sheen of all the golden vessels, all the burnished bronze, the diadems of the princes, the gilt thread of the embroideries on the robes of the architheoroi. One of the members of the Olympian Council stood up and with a sign of the hand stopped those who were still pressing forward.

These were no more state processions, only private pilgrims who were of no account. They now stood on the processional road amidst the dung of the animals and the trampled flowers that the column had left behind. Among these too there were grades and an order of precedence; the poorest were to be found at the extreme end beyond the wall of the Altis. Often they did not even have sacrificial animals, but only figures of bulls and rams in dough or wax. Happy in some degree that the sight of their poverty did not offend the god, they sat about on the ground, enmeshed in a faint patient whisper.

Meanwhile the priests were approaching the altar.

This was a high truncated cone, earthy grey in colour. Except for the stone kerb which surrounded its base in the form of a great ellipse, it had no inner foundation of masonry. It had piled up from the unremoved remnants of sacrifices through centuries and from the ashes that had been swept out from the hearth of Hestia in the prytaneion. Every year, in the month of the stag, Elaphios, the Olympian soothsayers would collect these ashes, mix them with water and plaster the slopes of the mound with the paste. The water of the Alpheios, containing large quantities of lime and chalk, made this coating proof against the winter rains. The mound was so hard that steps cut in its sides were as firm as if the slopes had been of rock.

These steps led up to the terrace, which, projecting out all around the cone, divided it into two unequal parts, the upper portion that was the smaller resting on the terrace like a formless eminence. The priests and the soothsayers mounted to the terrace while their assistants and the servitors with the animals waited at the foot of the altar. On this heap of ashes the woodcutter of the sacred grove arranged a pile of logs that had been cut to the measure prescribed in the ritual, and a theokolos threw into the middle a glowing firebrand taken from the hearth of Hestia. The white poplar wood was slow in kindling and the xyleus kept fanning it.

A theokolos, turning round to the gathering, cried: "Euphemeite!"

This word, ordering collectedness and quiet, opened the divine service. The spondauloi began playing on the flutes, to drown all profane sounds. One of the priests' servitors took up with both hands a large kettle of water and, starting from the right, carried it round the altar. Having returned to his original position, he went on to the terrace. The theokolos took a firebrand from the hearth and immersed it in the kettle. The water hissed at its fiery caress. The priests, by turns, dipped their hands into this water which had been consecrated by the immortal flame. A second servitor handed to the theokolos on a silver tray grains of barley parched with salt.

"Are those gathered here devoted to the gods?" inquired the high priest.

The spondauloi had stopped playing, so that everybody might hear the question; all answered: "Yes!" "Verily!" "With all our hearts!" or by a short adjuration in the name of the gods, and the throng buzzed with these cries of assent for several minutes. When the din abated, the priest scattered some handfuls of barley into the gathering and exclaimed: "Let us pray!"

The flutes began again while the first bull was led to the altar. The theokolos came down from the terrace, strewed barley over its head and cut off a tuft of hair from the forehead with a pair of golden scissors, thus consecrating the animal for the sacrifice. After this he went back to the top and threw the animal's hair into the fire.

There was heard a muffled bellow, the thud of the falling body and dying groans—the bull had been struck down with an axe. Its throat was cut also and a full goblet of fresh blood passed up the chain of spondophoroi to the top, where the fringe of the hearth was sprinkled with it. The assistants of the priests, with incredible quickness, moved the cumbrous carcass of the bull aside. They skinned and chopped it, cut out the fat, hacked off the thighs. The haunches they covered with fat, wrapped in the hide and carried to the theokolos. The priest, with the offering in his hand, turned to face the crowd, saying, "Let us pray!"

Then, placing the sacrificial flesh on the glowing logs with uplifted arm, he began to recite:

"Father Zeus, who reignest over Olympia——" and though nothing was heard below of his words, which floated away into the distance, into the crackle of the fire, into the music of the flutes, each one could repeat them in his mind: first the litany of the chief god's titles, and then the petition that he should accept this sacrifice from the men of Elis and grant his protection to them and to their country, and to all creatures that comprised their wealth, remove from them all evil, war, pestilence, fire, and grant that the aged folk enjoy as long as possible the sun's light in a thriving household amidst children and grandchildren.

The prayer embraced everything that man can hope for from the world, all its charms and blessings—but each one could add any personal wish. Whispers arose in which prayers were made for health and for Olympic wreaths and so on down to the most insignificant things such as are secreted in the recesses of the house.

Only Eleans were praying. It behoved nobody to meddle with their sacrifice and their discourse with the god. The others' turn would come when they should stand before the altar. Suddenly the flutes became silent and the theokolos terminated the prayer in an unexpected way:

"And dispel contention and confusion from us, that we may honour thee with the name of Lord of Peace and Saviour. Subdue in us envy and suspicion through which conflicts are born. Reconcile all Hellenes, imbue them with the wine of friendship and turn their hearts towards mercy and kindness."

These words caused surprise, but their significance was comprehended. It seemed that the soil of Greece itself gave utterance through them, the very heart of their native soil which, mangled by the Persian war, had created between the peoples for the first time a comradeship in arms. Nowhere could they have been more fitting than in this place whence every fourth year had issued forth the token of a universal truce, where the mere thought of war was considered a crime, where for the short spell of a few days one lived in a world free of frontiers.

Having heard these words to the end, many raised their hands, joining in the prayer. Some, however, taken aback by its unusual trend, gazed at the exegetes, filled with qualms because of this variance from the ritual. The faces of the exegetes were serene. The words of the theokolos were no novelty for them. In the Olympian tradition they had been repeated many times, different ages had heard them spoken over this altar, the ashes of which were more durable than human hopes.

The old Iamid still kept a watchful eye on the burning sacrifice. The gleam of the fire, the spurting of the flames, the smell of the skin and of the flesh, and lastly the smoke in all its drifts, as it curled, unrolled and ascended, each circumstance of its fading he marked and turned over in his mind, endeavouring to recognise from these signs the will of the god. They were propitious.

"Zeus has accepted the sacrifice," he said, "having at heart the happiness and weal of the people and the land of the Eleans."

But down below new heads of cattle had already been slaughtered and every few moments fresh goblets of blood and haunches covered with fat were being passed to the top. The spondauloi continued to play without once removing the flutes from their lips, the priests were singing hymns. The slaves were gathering up the slaughtered beasts and carrying them away to the kitchen in the prytaneion. The groups of pilgrims which stood before the temple of Hera kept pressing together to make way for them. The number of the animals was counted; there were sixty.

The sacrifices of the various states and colonies of the whole Greek world began after the hecatomb of the Eleans. One after another, the processions approached the altar in the order in which they had arrived and had taken up their position on the stadium. At the head of each were an architheoros and proxenos. The proxenos, appointed by the state that had chosen him as its representative before its particular god, was an Elean citizen. This was because Zeus, ruling over Olympia, though he was believed to be the same god whom the whole world worshipped, was at the same time especially the god of Olympia, of a definite place in the Elean country, and so no stranger had the right of access to him. The proxenos, therefore, was the intermediary between his country's god and the sacrifices of those who had appointed him.

Standing before the altar, he would lay his palm upon the shoulder of the architheoros, who was the representative of a whole country and people—Athens, Sparta, or Syracuse—introducing him and recommending him to his deity. Only then would the architheoros begin the hymn and make a sign to his people to lead in the animals. He himself would cut a tuft of hair from them and scatter the handfuls of barley, but a theokolos would take the haunches for the sacrifice from him and place them on the fire. The old Iamid after every sacrifice would peer into the flames and assign the prophecies to the towns, the islands, the archipelagoes and the distant shores represented before the altar.

The xyleus worked in the sweat of his brow, constantly feeding the fire with new logs. Slaves were continually bringing fresh bundles of wood from the stores and the xyleus would allot some for each procession and collect payment. At his side stood a good-sized bronze receptacle which was already half filled with coins. A part of this he would contribute to the Olympic treasury, but the remainder would be sufficient for purchasing fields, vineyards and a house. The processions, in addition, presented gifts for Olympia itself. Beside the altar a pile of money, which was guarded by the epimeletes, had already heaped up. But Hieron, having laid down his offering, ordered the gold mounts on the

horns of his bulls to be removed and instead of money
he threw these in. Thereafter everybody approaching
the altar laid some costly article before the epimeletes:
diminutive goblets, clasps, rings, shoulder-badges. Gerenos, who led the procession from Naukratis, presented a
fine large cauldron on a tripod beaten out of gold whereon, between two lions, the Oriental goddess Anaitis with
her great wings appeared in bas-relief.

The day was nearing noon. Whole herds of bulls and
rams had been slaughtered, great pools of blood had
been spilt on all sides of the altar. The altar itself was
dripping with blood, the steps leading on to the terrace
were red and slippery. The road by which the flesh had
been carried out to the camp, past the statues of the victors, was covered with glaring patches. The effluvium of
blood hovered over Olympia, and the air, heavily
charged with its odour, attracted kites which started
circling about in graceful gliding flight.

The three theokoloi relieved one another without
interrupting the ceremonies, while every now and then
the kathemerothytes would replace them, but all of them
were completely worn out. The spondauloi, out of
breath, removed the flutes from lips that had become
pale and hard as wood, and when there was no music,
no singing nor prayers, in that moment of sudden silence
only the crackle of the fire and the sizzle of the fat dripping on to the glowing coals were heard. Ever and anon
the flames would dwindle and be engulfed in the
columns of smoke which made the eyes smart with
pungent fumes.

On the terrace there was a dreadful heat not cooled
by even the slightest breeze; the whole world stood in

the blaze of the unchanging August weather. The priests appeared like ministers of hell in their gory vestments, their faces blackened with soot, their eyes staring, and surrounded by assistants who were quartering the sacrifices and looked as if they had bathed in blood. Only one of them, the chief of the Iamidai, a noble veteran, betokening eternal things, stood there fresh and calm; fatigue had not touched his handsome features. Allowing no one to take his place, tireless he kept gazing into the fire and peering into the entrails of the sacrificed animals, and when he turned round to utter his prophecies the calm glance of his eyes, blue as the heavens, shone out over the throng.

The stadium at last emptied. The processions, having offered their sacrifices, had returned to the camp. Now came the turn of the common pilgrims. But when they made a move from the Heraion, the priests began to leave the altar. Only the kathemerothytes and the xyleus remained, and the latter raised his price for wood. Quarrels and bargaining ensued. Elean citizens were hired by single persons to be their proxenoi and two obols for each sacrifice was demanded as payment for the flute players. The exegetes called to them to hurry up, for Zeus did not receive prayers in the afternoon. Hence curtailed rituals were performed, in which the animals went under the knife with the rapidity of a slaughter-house.

Many, unable to press through, searched for other altars, which abounded on all sides. At each there stood a priest who, with a nod, would invite the pilgrims. For one obol he would kindle a small fire with dry twigs and would himself serve as intermediary between the deity and the new arrival. He would perform his part honestly, he would compose long prayers, he would even join in the responses with them, and occasionally he would sing a few stanzas of a hymn, the old, partly understood words of which seemed to be borrowed from the speech of the gods. For the most part incense was burned and a few goblets of wine were poured, but there were some who put into the fire wax figures of the animals that were favoured by the deities; for Apollo cakes in the shape of a bow or a lyre, for Heracles large cucumbers with bits of wood stuck in them to represent the legs, horns and ears of an animal.

The whole of Olympia was burning and smoking, everywhere hands were raised to heaven and prayers were being loudly recited. However, when the sun had visibly passed its meridian, the priests departed from the altars and the crowd began to disperse. The sacred grove remained, a littered desolation. The smoke, vapour and smell from the burnings mingled with the odour of putrefying blood, discarded offal, entrails and dung. Ashes and soot floated in the air and even some of the trees that stood nearest the altar had been smirched by the fumes.

Yet the slaves with their rakes, shovels and wheelbarrows were already being hard pressed by the agoranomoi; some cartloads of sand had arrived; the altars were being washed down with sponges. The kites were snatching up bits of offal and flying off with them into the hills. A light evening wind cleared the sky.

In the purified air new smells were noticeable—of roasting meat, of olive-oil, of spices. These came thick and thicker, from the thousands of spits and kettles on the resinous smoking hearths. Having fasted since dawn, the pilgrims gazed hungrily on all that fried and sizzled or boiled in bronze pots, so slowly—would it never be cooked? The men kept feeding the fire with sticks, whole armfuls of brushwood, whole pine branches, every bit of fuel that fell into their hands; they would burn up carriages and tents—the sky caught fire and blazed with a huge conflagration.

At last they took the meat off the spits and lifted the lids of the kettles. From the turf ovens came the fragrance of fresh bread, honest and confident that the heavens would receive it. On planks propped up by stones, on casual chests, on the boxes of the carriages, or on mother earth itself stood smoking platters, round and well-stocked like the world. In painted pitchers the golden wine sparkled. On earthen jars beads of clear water glistened like the dew.

Having feasted his gods, man approaches their table, eats what they ate, drinks from the vessels on which the touch of their lips has not yet dried. Partaking of the sacrificial flesh, he enters into communion with the deities and establishes a co-existence with that heavenly race whose origin, as also the origin of all things, once lay in the depths of Chaos. This flesh enshrines the whole round world. The feaster absorbs with every mouthful springs, clouds, the sun, and the fertile germinating soil; from the marrow he sucks out the winds blowing in the grasses; between his teeth are crunched the four seasons of the year; through his veins flows the full cycle of existence, the incomprehensible mystery of metamorphoses, the eternal vicissitudes from the unbegotten stage to living nature, and his stomach digests the atoms, at whose birth the stars came forth in the confusion of the ages.

Rid of the spits and tripods, the hearths consumed the incense with a crackle and snorted out sharp-scented smoke. Reddened by the blaze of the hearths and an internal glow the people rose, laughing and shouting: "Tenella! Tenella!" This refrain of the old song of Archilochos, the song of Olympic champions, converted the wild cacophony into a melodious stanza; from Hieron's tent the voice of Pindar burst forth, his ode of victory spread itself with peacock splendour across a momentary silence that formed about him; the silvery purl of the harp sparkled like a fountain playing under a bush of stars. Along the sky moved the moon—a chalice filled with the nectar of the night.

. . . .

The camp was astir at daybreak. Dawn drove the athletes to the stadium, but it did not dispel their drowsiness. The night of meat and wine had dulled their senses. The entry of the competitors, the proclamation of the heralds and the first races took place in semi-darkness; men's minds, like shopmen's shutters, were but half open so early. Skamandros of Mytilene won, in a complete silence, and departed with the wreath lonely and astonished that the labour of many years, the measureless space which he had run in training his legs, were summed up in a few deep breaths and in a spell so brief and soundless.

The world was not fully awake till the next race. The sun had emerged from behind the heights of Pisa. The brightened stadium flickered with the shadows of the runners. This was the diaulos, the double race, from the

275

start to the goal and back. Divided into two groups of six, the competitors glided rapidly past, and equally swift was the duel of the winners of the heats. The wreath was won by Dandis of Argos. His name clanged to the heavens like a bell.

The dolichos, the long distance, run over twenty-four stades, was announced.

There were seven competitors, all young men; the eldest, Timodemos of Achatnai, was twenty-eight years of age. Their bodies, each efficient and splendid in itself, when taken together formed a striking collection of dissimilar elements, as if the spirit of the race, in its search for a perfect shape, had carefully considered the angularities, planes and curves, had gauged the growth, deducted fleshy and bony substances, until it had arrived at the slim figure, the gentle arch of the chest, the narrow hips, the wiry long-striding legs, with which it had endowed a few of them. But did it really dwell within them, this capricious spirit which so often disregards magnificent human fabrics and settles in humble bodies, hidden in the chamber of the heart, at the bottom of the lungs, in the damp porticoes of the blood and the secretions?

The modern long-distance race, describing an uninterrupted ellipse, is quite different from the Greek dolichos, which had no laps. The competitors, stationed across the whole breadth of the stadium, ran in straight parallel lines, with wide intervals between each other. Having reached the line marked out at the end of the track, they turned about at that spot and on the same course over their own traces they ran back. At each return Kapros cut a sign with a stilus on a clay tablet, counting the stades like measured ells of cloth.

The smooth surface was grooved by seven furrows trodden out by the runners which, extending between the two lines marked out at the start and at the goal, gave the whole track the resemblance of a seven-stringed lyre. The young naked bodies flew along in the furrows with the velocity of a sound wave. They were impelled by a uniform rhythm, the equal cadence of their tread, which was accompanied by the soft crunch of the gravelly sand. This was the most entertaining part of the races, these first stades, equal and excellent, when each was fresh, brimming with hope, when all of them reached the end and turned back on the new flight at the same time, halting for an instant at the line slightly bent as if they were about to plunge into the surge of a river. And really there was some current in the air, in the people, some refreshing breath pervaded the crowd, the track appeared to be a lake or a sunny bay on which seven narrow boats sped past with the measured splash of oars.

But this blissful state of evenness and peace was short-lived. At a certain moment the line of the run started undulating and warping. Among the runners this and that one began losing a trifle of space on each stade; he would reach the line a faint fraction of time later than another and these fragments would multiply and grow and would leave him farther and farther behind.

The seven runners began to spread out and the track changed into a chessboard with a quaint game in progress where the pawns kept on their line without interrupting their onward course, while the players sat on the heights in a crowd of many thousands and with a shout tried to guide their pawns which were slipping away from them. Poseidonia and the island of Samos shouted the loudest, embittered by the sight of their competitors, who had begun to lag from the sixth stade.

There were two fires of intense and unflagging energy; one in the first track, in which Ergoteles was running, and the other in the seventh, which the Spartan Ladas occupied. From the very beginning they had taken up a sharp pace which would have deserved praise in a sprint, and this they had forced upon the rest. Nobody was capable of maintaining this for long. A while after the Samian and the Poseidonian, another two fell behind to plough their furrow patiently and hopelessly.

Timodemos was the only one who would not give in. Occupying the fourth track, in the very centre of the course, he oscillated between Ladas and Ergoteles like the indicator of a weighing machine. He was truly high-spirited and the confidence of all Attica supported him. But the manner in which he made use of it showed that Timodemos's soul was not the equal of his body. For his body was rigid, too rigid for a sprinter, it was appropriate for a more strenuous struggle, with its hard musculature it would have endured even the pancration. The soul, on the other hand, was light and vacant. Each shout swelled into a storm within him, it emboldened him, but the lead of a few paces which brought him to the forefront of the trio and kindled the spectators' enthusiasm had deprived him of all moderation. With deep draughts he drained himself as if the next stade was the last.

Only half of the race, however, was over. The spectators, waiting for further incidents, became quiet. In his heart Timodemos felt this tranquillity, agonising because of its coldness, and at the height of his speed, to which he had hurriedly risen, he was suddenly encompassed by the breath of a great space, the abyss of the remaining ten stades emitted the sound of an incompletely filled vacuum. By the force of the impetus he flew into it for some time, but already dusk was descending over him. Ergoteles and Ladas again loomed up on his horizon.

While Timodemos courageously exerted himself, the other two runners pursued their course calmly. They remained impassive, not allowing themselves to be swept away by another's will and not diminishing their own speed. Both were running at an identical pace, with arms bent at the elbows, with the chest thrust forward, with their heads raised high, and staring at some goal in front which appeared to be far outside the stadium.

They looked like two messengers, like those hemerodromoi whom a government, an army or a nation sends forth to remote places on some secret mission with no written message. Naked and unarmed, they find protection in the divine laws. Behind them stand Zeus, the patron of heralds, and Hermes, who himself is a messenger. With an equal breath they cut a passage for themselves through fields and vineyards, over marshy ground, and through forests, avoiding towns and villages. People make way for them, and dare not detain them. The sun accompanies them to the mountain defiles where they remain alone in the mysterious night, to run down at dawn into the valleys and carry their message to its goal, even though it were to be whispered with the last breath.

They were the wings of the world, for the world, the languid tranquil world of the fifth century, rolled on in the laborious ruts of ox-drawn carts. A horse, an ass or a mule served it to the limit of their endurance, but always a thicket, a lurking quagmire, a steep precipice, a number of things might bar the way which only man could overcome. The training-grounds of the palestras and the gymnasiums reared a noble race of couriers, devourers of space, who could not be overtaken, and the Games gave them the publicity whereby they might be located on the day when some new and unexpected Marathon should come.

In just such guise Ergoteles and Ladas displayed themselves to the world. Both were equal and perfect. The others were imperfect only by comparison with them. Of these, however, two were beneath such comparison. Having lost a whole stade, they were now running in the opposite direction, as if the spirit of the Games had turned its back on them. Timodemos fell back a hundred feet or so, which he was never again to make up. The air around him became more and more murky, he waded through it blear-eyed and with lips tasting of salt from the sweat which was pouring down his face. Occasionally his name would still burst forth from someone's lips, but it reached him as from a distance, stifled by the rush of blood in his temples, as if this too, the wondrous portion of man, wished to forsake him at the last moment.

The end of the run was nearing. The spectators stood up, unable to keep seated under the stress of emotion. With Sparta were shouting the whole of Laconia, all the dependent towns and half of the Dorian tribes.

"La—das! La—das!"

The wild outcry, concentrated in this mighty spondee, smote the stadium like a sledge-hammer.

Ergoteles felt all the strokes upon himself. They thrashed the world, the sun scattered showers of sparks which seemed to burn his eyes. His legs became stiff and numb, they found no support on the earth which had renounced him. A terrible loneliness chilled him to the marrow. Torn away from his Cretan ancestors, having no blood-tie with his new fatherland, Himera, he continued to belong only to himself, a possession to which no one had any right. The shouts raining upon Ladas expressed the sacred right of a tribe, of a country, of a community, of a soil enriched with the ashes of the dead, a just claim to his muscles, to the throb of his heart, to the breath of his lungs; Ergoteles was stripped of the earth like a soul whose body had not been interred, he was a phantom sentenced to woeful and gloomy wandering. He experienced a conviction of utter uselessness.

He ran on aware of nothing, automatically. The torrent of outcries carried him into a limitless void. Finding himself at the end of the track, he took a few paces more as if he intended to run off it. At that moment the shrill sound of the trumpet announced the last stade. Ergoteles turned round and drifted back into his track.

Through one of those marvels which fill the soul of a true athlete, he shrouded himself with a serene brightness. It was the composure of a man who had been cast overboard and ordered to ride the rocking waves, and who had suddenly perceived that he could do so in reality and that the water did not give way under him. The world was seething, convulsing, howling as of yore, it seemed all the winds of heaven had united their forces to extinguish him, but he kept on running in his furrow as if he were a tongue of flame coursing along a trail of oil on the ground.

Ladas carried off the victory. Those few paces which he had gained at the moment when Ergoteles had run beyond the line in a daze and was late for the last stade were all that he won by.

"If you had wanted you could have had the wreath," said Ladas, as they stood before the altar of Zeus.

Ergoteles, remaining silent, embraced his shoulder. Ladas's heart with its deep-toned beats said more than words could have expressed.

The spectators became suddenly quiet, as though sleep had overtaken them. In spite of the victory the race was not over yet. The Olympian law required that each one, under pain of a flogging, should carry out the task that he had undertaken. Five competitors were plodding along on the stadium, running doggedly to their goal, about which nobody cared any longer; no attention was paid to their noble effort, their faultless posture or their graceful movements. When the last of them had finished, half of the Spartans present at the spectacle left their places. They all gathered around Ladas, who, already wreathed, was carried on their shoulders to the camp.

The first part of the programme, in the earliest part of the day, was finished. There was no interval, the wrestlers were summoned at once. The stadium shrank into the small arena used for the bouts, and together with it the world narrowed, closed in by the ever hotter sun. For a start, Eurymenes circled Pataikos in the grasp of his long arms and thereby took the breath out of the spectators' lungs.

Their chamydes and chitons chafed their bodies, so

they threw them back and sat half naked. Their muscles were quivering. Every move of the wrestlers stirred their blood, which coursed in their veins like a song of their own youth. As often as someone fell on the stadium, the heights breathed heavily, as if all were being crushed by the same fate.

In such wise Pataikos, Epharmostos and Eurymenes suffered their discomfitures. Gerenos astonished them and struck them with awe. The giant, covered with thick black hair, looked like a creature of the myths, like one of those sylvan men, the guardians of the flocks of the gods, with whom Heracles had wrestled. He had no adversaries to match his measure. His victory was inevitable and unjust, like the havoc that is wrought by the force of the elements.

How rich the day is! The boxers are coming out. The casting of lots reserved Euthymos for the end, one might say, as a good host does, who, after the light wine, offers a jar of a strong and mature vintage.

Philon and Menalkes took their stand opposite each other as if at the two sides of a loom and started beating the air with light feints. They misled each other with their eyes which looked elsewhere than at the spot where the hands wished to strike; the outstretched palms, like those of the blind, groped about in space. Their nimble legs leaped hither and thither. The clenched fists gathered the blows which were showered around into the void.

The skull, the eyes, the nose, the jaw, the ears, the most valuable parts of man's anatomy, are disregarded by the rules. These shield, however, the neck, the chest and all the rest of the body. Seemingly cruel, the Olympic rules made the contest a purely dramatic display of skill.

The target for the blows was so limited, so easy to cover up, that thousands of leads never got home.

The spectators began to warm up as the bout progressed. They breathed with a passion so fierce that the fighters, in comparison with them, seemed completely calm.

.　　.　　.　　.　　.　　.　　.　　.

Let us tarry here.

The Games began at dawn and it is now noon. Through eight full hours, according to our own modern measurement of time, the exciting and impetuous spectacle lasts. There are no intervals except those which the rite imposes upon itself, the introduction of the competitors, the conferences of the judges and the giving of wreaths. Nobody leaves his place.

These curious people have forgotten their hunger, though occasionally they take a draught of water into their hot mouths. They endure the heat as if they were sitting under ostrich-feathered fans. Like some strange manifestation of ephemeral mayflies whose whole life is narrowed into the organ of vision, into the function of looking and experiencing. Always eager for more, they greet each pair of competitors with the same enthusiasm, their souls are kneaded between the fists of the contestants, and they drain yet another hour of the August afternoon without scalding their throats. On the contrary, their throats are vocal and powerful when Euthymos, son of Astykles, receives the wreath for boxing.

There followed, without an interval, the pancration, a combination of boxing and wrestling in which everything was permitted, in which even death might be expected, though it never occurred, for two splendid bodies, trained and expert, counter-poised each other like the two electrical poles.

The herald announced the bout between Theagenes of Thasos and the Athenian Kallias. Both entered the enclosure of the aleiptai, who were waiting for them with water, olive-oil, a sponge and towel. Thirty thousand pairs of eyes devoured each of their movements, the common routine of washing, rubbing, adjusting the shoulder strap, as a crowd of worshippers in the gigantic nave of a church observes the deacons clothe the bishops in their pontifical vestments.

Theagenes was the first to take up his position on the sand. From the thick ankles up to the hard round skull he was built entirely of effective essentials. Every atom had gone to make up the strength and endurance of his torso. He raised his fist, and all felt that not a single blow would be wasted.

We are looking at our unquiet nervous watch, at our frail time that has been crushed into minute fractions—it is approaching three in the afternoon. Who will swoon first? Where is the legendary death of the philosopher Thales, who had died at Olympia a hundred years before from sunstroke? Maybe one of the greybeards? But look, the oldest of them, Damaretos of Heraea, comes out from the shade of one of the treasury vestibules in order to be nearer to the race in arms which is going to begin. He considers this race, in some measure, as his own, for he originated it forty years ago. He shades his eyes with his hand as if he would recognise amidst the glittering bronzes which the servitors are bringing, the helmet, the shield and the greaves, his memorable accoutrements of victory. But the helmets and shields cannot be told apart, and the greaves are not to be seen. They are not there. Eight nude runners are making for the start with helmets on their heads and with shields on their left arms.

"Nowadays, father, they run like that," said Theopompos, his son. "Kapros has abolished the wearing of greaves."

Damaretos snorted, one might have thought that the intensely rarified air of the new period was irritating to his nostrils:

"Oh! That is surely the work of that Astylos!"

He was not the only one against Astylos. Twelve Crotonians were howling with rage. This man, who in three Olympiads had given his town, Croton, six olive wreaths, had renounced his fatherland and was now running as a Syracusan. He ran desperately well, straight to the goal which, for the seventh time, yielded to him like a dog. Gryllos came second, Telesikrates third. In the midst of thirty thousand yells the cry of the Crotonians was lost like a voiceless purr. But those who stood nearest them heard distinctly:

"Traitor!" "Hieron has bought him like a horse!" "I shall name my mule Astylos!" "At home he has a house which the town awarded him. The house ought to be pulled down and the site ploughed over!" "Or it should be turned into a prison!"

Yes, Hieron had actually purchased Astylos. But for how much? Something was said about a score of talents. The news spread like wildfire, the shouts died down, people stared at each other, perturbed. Never had a similar incident occurred within the memory of man. The wreath should not be awarded to him! Kapros, however, summoned him to the tent and braided on his brow three sprigs of wild olive.

. . . .

The Games were over. The night and day that followed belonged to the victors. The island of Lesbos, whose capital Mytilene had been covered with fame by Skamandros, Argos by Dandis, Sparta by Ladas, Tarentum by Ikkos, the island Thasos by Theagenes, the island of Chios by little Glaukos, Ægina by Theognetos, Athens by Kallippos, the victor in the kalpe, advanced in separate groups, the victor covered all over with fillets, in the midst of them and with the flute players at his side. The old song of Archilochos was sung:

> O Tenella! Herakles, thou glorious ruler, hail!
> Tenella, glorious victor!
> Hail, Iolaos, comrade true!
> O Herakles, thou glorious ruler, hail!

Full of song, the groups proceeded along the streets of the camp and along the river. They returned to the sacred grove and went out upon the roads which led to the outer world. The Lokrians from Italy, intoxicated by their double victory, made the most noise. Agesidamos and Euthymos had won for them the rank of the best boxers in the world. The princes were banqueting in their tents. The immense tent of Hieron was entertaining Astylos, and till far into the night the peculiar light of a hundred olive lamps filtered through the purple walls.

At dawn the champions were summoned to the sacred grove. Headed by the hellanodikai and the priests, they went in procession, pausing at the six altars dedicated to the twelve gods. Each one in turn offered a libation and a handful of incense. After that, taking the road by which they had come, they returned to the prytaneion, where the Olympian authorities entertained the victors at a solemn feast.

The tents had already been rolled up. The truce of the gods had taken a scant measure of time for itself. Before the month elapsed, the road between the numerous boundaries, opposing rights and endless quarrels, would be broken into sections. Hence the hurry. Within two days all the highways would be covered with dust.

The competitors, prior to their departure, went to the bank of the Alpheios and threw into the water wreaths of poplar, pine, and olive-sprigs. These were like hieroglyphs of the Olympic soil to which they wished to return. The swift current snatched them up and bore them rapidly away, while the competitors ran along the bank as long as they had sufficient breath, until they lost sight of their wreaths round some bend. A few wreaths, however, would stop on their course, detour round the eddies, move in a circle at the shallows—what wonderful luck!—and the current would carry them to the opposite bank and leave them in a safe nook.

A few days later the last carriage disappeared behind the heights. Olympia reverted to its usual loneliness, a curious settlement situated, so it seemed, nearer to heaven than to the earth. As compared with the gods who dwelt here, the people constituted a mere handful: a few priests, the kleiduchos, a few officials at the treasury, the xyleus, a few servants, altogether a score or so of families, hidden in small houses beyond the sacred grove. Four years of uneventful silence lay ahead of them.

In the valley at the riverside there remained a mound of rubbish, the litter of all those days during which tens of thousands of people had lived, eaten and digested here. For a time some of the Olympic servants loitered about in search of things which might be of some use. This and that one picked up a handful of obols, while the earth had swallowed as many more for the benefit of future archaeologists. The wind blew the rags away and the rains washed off the impurities. Finally Alpheios, eternal master of the land, would overflow his banks in winter floods.

EPILOGUE

ETERNAL time had recited the rosary of the months and again the same full moon is leading people from the extremities of the world. Familiar faces have returned. Sodamos, Eurymenes, Kallias, Ergoteles, Epharmostos, Menalkes, Gryllos, Sotion, all lived to see their wreaths. The latest, little Xenophon, did not grow tall enough to touch the Olympic olive till twelve years had passed. Telesikrates consoled himself with the Delphic laurel. After that they disappeared into life, into the rich magnificent life of the fifth century B.C., like harvesters into high corn.

Ikkos, for a long series of Olympiads, never missed attending the Games. He always sat in some treasury among the guests of honour. Victory had brought him much more than he had expected to squeeze out from his obdurate uncles. He forsook Tarentum and travelled widely over the world. He visited palestras and gymnasiums, where, for a good remuneration, he taught the attainment of bodily perfection. He was listened to as though he were an infallible oracle. He educated a whole school of trainers, who within the span of one generation transformed the life of Greek sport.

They really were masters of their art. The bodies entrusted to their care were subjected to purposeful and suitable methods. Within a brief period of observation

they would unerringly calculate the physical bent whereby they were able to train their pupils for a fitting pursuit.
Under their guidance nobody lost his way nor groped,
but went straight to the end in view and usually won.
He who was to be a runner was so from the first moment;
the wrestler, the boxer or the pancratiast lived in his
own sphere under different conditions, they had separate
times for practices and were directed differently. What
the young men of Sotion's time had considered a noble
pastime, the spilling of a few drops from the overabun-
dance of their youth, became a serious and responsible
undertaking. Revelling in the unlimited use of native
energy was not permitted, everything was regulated for
a definite reason.

These new training-grounds looked like a nursery, or
a stud-farm for breeding dogs, where the pure strain of
the various species is carefully guarded. Unique specimens were born with whom the average being could not
compare. Men heard with astonishment of exceptional
discus throws, leaps, weight-lifting, of the unprecedented
strength of wrestlers; and before they had calmed down,
fresh news still more amazing would arrive from other
gymnasiums. Across the whole Greek world scores of
names laden with renown passed from mouth to mouth,
and their engagements were awaited with an impatience
that was quite understandable.

There were considerably more Games now and they
attracted such immense crowds as had never gathered
before. Every town, often in the year, during the holy
festivals, would arrange contests, for which they tried
to capture these prodigies of the human race. The most
famous among them learned to make difficulties or

refuse; on more than one occasion the insignificant reward was not worth the long journey they would have to undertake. Each of them had in his possession an abundance of wreaths, fillets, and other manifold distinctions, without mentioning the money, things that had a saleable value and other benefits, such as houses awarded by grateful towns and pensions for life. There were no words lofty enough to describe their glory. Every second one was "the foremost athlete of all times", they bestowed on themselves the title of "successor to Heracles", their gravestones bore long litanies of the most glowing adjectives. It was judged, however, that nothing could fittingly reward them for the honour they were conferring upon mankind by belonging to it although the speed of their legs or the strength of their fists gave them the right to be classed among superhuman beings. They brought still greater honour to the state of which they were citizens, and they knew how to express this honour, in keeping with the example of Astylos, in terms of a definite sum of money. More than one ultimately became citizens of the world, so often they would claim different descents on different occasions.

The average man, having spent his tender years in a palestra, as was proper for a decent Hellene, looked upon these new gymnasiums with envy. He felt as wild flowers might feel on seeing, through the panes of a hot-house, creatures like themselves but growing to unheard-of heights of glory, thanks to special conditions.

By the very odours that came from their kitchens the costliness of their system of life might be deduced. The average man lived on vegetables, cheese, fruit and fish; meat he would see only on some festive occasion:

here, on the contrary, a never-ending banquet steamed from the large cooking-pans. How poor and simple was that dish of Ikkos which had so stirred the Elean gymnasium! Undoubtedly it had belonged to a species that was not worthy of these tables. Moreover, Ikkos himself had drifted ever further into the shadow of the past. A hundred years after his death he seemed to his own descendants a strange ancestor, belonging to a backward and lowly era.

In the new gymnasiums each had his particular diet, the runner, the boxer, the wrestler, each his own. The last-mentioned nourished himself with meat in order to augment the bulk and weight of his body. Special messes of pork, fat, sea-food, wheat rolls with poppy-seed were chosen to make up his portion. Besides, this diet was measured out and calculated by a doctor, who took care of his digestion, his evacuations, and in more urgent cases would examine the nature of the faeces. In the bath-room the balneologist would not leave him alone. Every day had its sitz-baths, shower-baths, short moments of steam-baths and lightning dips into cold tubs. These were graded according to the fatness and the constitution of the athlete in question. Even the stars whose constellations shone at his birth were taken into account. And after that, hours for walks were appointed, sleep was ordered, unnecessary movement was prohibited; the course of training, in fact, was set out on elaborately scheduled tablets so that not a single particle of the energy in these precious human bulks might be wasted. Their existence moved between table, bed, bath and the hands of a masseur. They were never left without supervision any more than children, giant children it is true, but with the frailty of childhood which any breeze of life could cut short.

All this was much too expensive and there were not many who could take advantage of such extravagances. Life had to be renounced for these conditions as in a monastery, and, doing no productive work, it was necessary for the athlete to possess means in order to keep himself over many years. Only wealthy people or those who hoped to recover their capital outlay from profits to come could afford it. The career of an agonist came to be a separate profession, very profitable and highly esteemed. Of course, this was not talked of openly, it was even considered thoroughly bad taste to harbour the suspicion that the competitors were seeking material gain. Thousands of pretexts were concocted to facilitate for them a life hovering between strict virtue and grand incomes.

A nation which half a century earlier had consisted more or less of competitors only, in which each citizen not a hopeless cripple was prepared to enter for any event in the stadium and preserved this ability up to the threshold of old age, suddenly renounced these ambitions to the advantage of a selected handful. A general opinion took root that, sport being such a complicated, such a difficult affair, because under ordinary conditions it was impossible to ensure in practice the irrational achievement of records, the best thing to do would be to remain on the bench of the spectators amidst passive emotions. The first effort made was to secure these benches, and the stadiums were enlarged by comfortable rows of seats.

These allowed the protracted spectacles to be more easily endured, but they did not afford a shelter from ennui. This guest, unknown in previous centuries, now accompanied the races and pentathlon, which in spite of everything preserved a considerable importance, although in their simplicity they seemed to be languid and colourless. The essential items of the Games consisted of wrestling, boxing and the pancration; these were the chief dishes, copious and heavy like the over-nourished huge bodies which stepped forth to contend. The boxer became the earliest idol of the crowd, but on condition that he spared neither the blood of his opponents nor his own. Special gloves served him for this purpose, but how different from the soft leather straps which formerly had protected the fingers! They were of hard, thick leather having multiple folds and so shaped that in them the fist struck like a weapon of iron, smashing noses and ears and shattering jaws. These were praiseworthy wounds, which sculptors would reproduce in bronze with the most zealous exactness.

Art had to pass through the school of naturalism in order to evolve faithful representations of this new race. It produced figures with an astonishing and immense amount of flesh and muscle, sitting or leaning against a tree or a column, giving the impression of a strength that was strangely ineffective and seemed to be solely weight. And this art did not flinch from displaying their faces or from handing down some effigies absolutely bestial, with narrow foreheads, empty eyes, flattened noses and lips composed of two shreds of flesh, the whole being lost in a wild growth of hair on the face. At the end of this gallery there appeared, in the times of the Roman Empire, portraits still more disgusting. These are met with on mosaics, where the athlete seems to represent some creature of other geological epochs, some ichthyosaurus-like human being with a gigantic body and an uncommonly small head in which it is difficult to imagine that a brain is lodged.

To mingle admiration for the professional agonist with contempt was learned early enough. Everyone admitted that it was impossible to equal them, but nobody wished to be like them. Self-respecting youth did not dream of wreaths other than those which could be acquired by letting one's own horses run in a race. Alkibiades, at Sotion's age, spent his days in his stable. Only in remote districts, which the new age had not touched, in Arcadia, in Epeiros, in Aetolia, even in Thessaly, there still existed gymnasiums in which the old spirit lived, and from these there came noble-minded competitors who still occasionally won a place in the annals of victory. Generally, however, sport evolved into gymnastic exercises and games for maturing youth, or it merely served to train soldiers.

Cicero, travelling across Greece, had expected to see these statues pacing in the streets. But he was astonished to find how very few young men in Athens could boast of good looks. One got accustomed to the sight of pale complexions, bent backs, narrow chests, spindle legs, flabby bellies and all the sorts and conditions of a decadent race pent up in great towns and in cramped houses. Ultimately, doctors prescribed modest doses of sport for a nation which was the first to open the eyes of the world to the beauty of a healthy body.

Amidst these changes Olympia continued to exist. Of the sacred grove there remained but the name, which was justified by a tuft of trees that had survived

around the sacred olive. The rest had been engulfed by
new buildings. The magnificent temple of Zeus sheltered
in its mighty interior the masterpiece of Phidias; porticoes and colonnades opened out on all sides. The statues
of victors pressed into every vacant space; there were
hundreds and finally thousands, a separate world. In
them lived the generation that was eternally young, a
generation untainted by any blemish.

Olympia yielded to the changing time, without re-
nouncing a single one of its dogmas. What had been inscribed on the sacred discus centuries ago was a law which
could be interpreted but not evaded. Conforming to the
new requirements, a palestra and a gymnasium had been
erected, and in them competitors did their training during the last days before the Games. Even the most shame-
less competitors took the old oath of noble sport and
generally they were true to it. The bribing of an opponent
was seldom resorted to, and if it was discovered the
culprits were punished with a heavy fine. For violating the
sacred truce Sparta had been proscribed from the Games.
Lichas, a member of a royal Spartan family, had been
publicly flogged for infringing the resolutions of the hellanodikai. Even the most difficult requisite, the Hellenic
ancestry of the competitors, was overcome. It was upheld
by the law, but for the new nations that claimed a right to
participate in the Games, suitable legitimisation was introduced. By such means Macedonia, then Rome and finally
almost the whole world was accepted to be of Greek
blood. Olympia's permanence acted as a factor in keeping up men's spirits, and in the worst times romantic
currents issued from it which turned the languishing
gymnasiums back to the old ideals.

This was no longer a noonday, but a humble borrowed light which was to suffice for whole centuries. An inextinguishable war tore the Greek tribes asunder, darkness encompassed the great powers, Alexander's sword ploughed through the East, the Roman eagles began to soar, but unremittingly Olympia claimed her truce during the festival of the full moon. While the rest of the world lived in a fierce glare, to relax in the serenity of the Elean country was a great relief. To some extent the few weeks of an untroubled existence made one realise that the world would not lose its charm, were people to cease thinking about exterminating each other. Periodically Olympia would become an actual League of Nations, a true one, for, instead of hypocritical diplomats and the secret ceremonial of conferences, she had at her disposal the conscience of all countries, which were represented by thousands of people from every station in life. In the first days of the Peloponnesian war the embassy of Mytilene lodged a complaint against the tyranny of Athens and demanded autonomy; Gorgias, the famous sophist, disclosed the treacherous collusions of Sparta with the Persian king; it was here that the innumerable treaties, alliances, and decrees concerning freedom were first declared and inscribed on stone slabs. Through Olympia led the straightest path to the regard and remembrance of mankind; there gathered figures great and small, ordinary and extraordinary; kings and Roman Caesars left their trace on her.

.   .   .   .

According to Greek chronology, the first Olympiad began in 776 B.C., and the last, the two hundred and ninety-third, ended in A.D. 393. One thousand one hundred and seventy years of life, an unparalleled span for any human institution. More than one nation has lacked breath to hold out on such a long road. But in the latter part of her long life, as is customary with all old people, Olympia exaggerated her years, and a discus with an inscription defining the age of the Games as twenty centuries has been preserved. The grandmother of Greek sport, she surpassed everything around her in vitality. The world which was created together with her had crumbled into ruins. The pilgrims' paths led through ruins, through towns of which the mere names remained, and through depopulated countries. Olympia herself was full of scars, the most valuable statues had forsaken her, many altars were extinguished as if death had even visited the heavens. Hellenic blood, disseminated over three continents, was seldom present in the veins of competitors. The last of the remembered victors did not possess one drop of it, not one drop of this noble priceless blood, which formerly did not brook the slightest adulteration, the purity of which was examined with such anxious scrupulousness. It was Varazdates, an Armenian prince, a descendant of the Arsacids, who in the year 385 received the wreath for boxing. In addition to being no Greek, he belonged to a community which in earlier days formed a part of the Persian kingdom, and it is possible that one of his ancestors, taken into captivity at Salamis or Plataeae, may have been among the slaves tending the horses in the days of the great seventy-sixth Olympiad.

It is difficult to imagine how the Games looked in these last years. They must, however, have been something which could not be disregarded, if ruling princes took part in them. Olympia did not die a natural death. In the year 393 a decree of the Emperor Theodosius I abolished the pagan festival. Doubtless it was read out during the Games. One of the high officials of the Christian monarch, standing on the terrace of the treasuries, commanded the gathering to return to their homes and the competitors to cover their nakedness. There were, undoubtedly, monks with him, who, following the example of St. Pachomius, opposed all gymnasiums, baths and personal cleanliness. These took away the keys of the temples from the priests, in order to batter the statues of the gods to smithereens and set fire to the buildings. About two years later Alarich, the leader of the Goths, retreating before the Byzantine general Stilicho, took shelter in the wooded mountain of Pholoe, just opposite Olympia. His barbarian hordes roamed about in the valley, they watered their horses in the Alpheios and peeped into the untenanted buildings in search of treasure. In the whole neighbourhood there was no longer a living soul.

Man, however, finds it difficult to forsake a spot which has served him for a very long period. In the fifth century Olympia was peopled again. The village, an everlasting element, weathering all reverses, propagating like a weed, built itself up with miserable hovels made from the ruins which were at hand. Peasants tilled the soil and gathered the grapes growing on the ranges. The studio of Phidias, a great brick building in which the sculptor had worked upon his Zeus, was made into a Byzantine church with three naves and an apse built into the east wall. The Heraion, the treasuries, the gymnasium, the palestra, the temple of Zeus and scores of other buildings still endured. They were used as fortresses at the times when the Vandals devastated the western shores of Greece.

But new people had already arrived. They came by the same track which once the first inhabitants of the land of Elis had taken, the route of all historical migrations, from the north to the south, and had crossed the narrow sea separating the Peloponnesus from Central Greece. These were the Slavs. The Greek tongue became silent and along the mountains and in the settlements, names which belong to the Polish language took a firm grip. The newcomers had arrived at an adverse time. The Peloponnesus shook twice during the course of the sixth century with strange tremors, as though it did not want to receive the foreign race. Of Olympia there remained not one stone upon another. What was not overthrown by the earthquake was overwhelmed by landslides from the heights. In the end the Alpheios and the Kladeos, having changed their beds through the recurring floods, covered the ruins with a layer of sand thirteen feet deep.

Complete desolation beset these sites. The valley was overgrown with thick undergrowth and the slopes were covered by woods. They were nourished by the moisture of the divine river which brought in its never-tiring current the coolness of the Arcadian defiles. The beaver, driven away long ago, returned and took refuge by the Alpheios, building its dam as in the days of the pile-dwellings of primitive man. Countless moons changed their shapes from the new to the full moon, unobserved by any eyes. Occasionally someone from the remoter settlements lying behind the heights, while hunting game, would stray amidst the myrtles and pines, but returning home would not be able to say where he had been: these regions had no name.

. . . .

In the year 1875, under the spades of German archaeologists, the ruins of Olympia began to appear. The excavations lasted six years. The remnants of the sacred circle lay at the bottom of the earth dug out, whitish-grey and disintegrated like bones in an open grave. But the spirit, entombed with them fifteen centuries before, was still alive. The discovery of Olympia became a watchword for the rebirth of the Games. The first attempts were made at Athens simultaneously with the beginning of the excavations. They were timid and beset with difficulties, as the beginnings of Olympia itself must have been in the old days. Soon, however, in the year 1896, the first Olympiad of the modern era was inaugurated. The spirit of Greek agonistics began its second life, to repeat once more all former virtues and errors.

GLOSSARY OF GREEK WORDS

Where a term is explained in the text itself, only the page reference is listed.

agora: market place, center of public life
agoranomoi: (police) market supervisors
akamaton pyr: untiring flame
Akara: p. 42
aleiptai: masseurs (often trainers and heads of a wrestling school)
amphora: two-handled, narrow-necked vessel for holding wine
Apite: go! (starting signal)
*architheoros (*pl. *architheoroi):* leader of a holy legation
*aryballos (*pl. *aryballoi):* pouchlike vessel
aulos: flute with mouthpiece

balbis: p. 50
bater: p. 48
bombylioi: narrow-mouthed bottles
Boötes: ox driver, a northern constellation containing the first magnitude star Arcturus
bouleuterion: courthouse

chiton: garment for both sexes, usually worn next to the skin
chlaina: blanket
*chlamys (*pl. *chlamydes):* short cloak
choinix: dry measure, a slave's daily allowance (of wheat)
cyathus: cup for drawing wine out of the bowl

Demeter Chamyne: goddess of the fertile earth
diaulos: p. 39
Dioskouroi: sons of Jupiter: Castor and Pollux
diphtera: p. 161
dolichos: p. 276
Droion: p. 42

Elaphios: p. 265
ephors: overseers

epimeletes: p. 179
eschara: p. 258
Euoe!: Bacchanalian exclamation
Euphemeite: p. 266
exegetes: p. 261

halteres: jumping weights
hellanodikai: p. 25
hellanodikeon: house of the hellanodikai
hemerodromoi: p. 279
Heraion: temple of Hera
hydria: (water) bucket

Iamidai: p. 258

kalpe: p. 240
kathemerothytes: p. 261
*kleiduchos (*pl. *kleiduchoi):* p. 183
kynodesmos: dog halter

leukoma: p. 193

mastigophoroi: p. 132
mazai: p. 156
medimnoi: corn measures, nearly twelve gallons
myrinites: p. 159

nomophylakes: guardians of the laws

opisthodomos: back chamber of a temple

pancratiast: contender in the pancration
pancration: p. 67
peplos: richly adorned garment carried by priestesses in solemn procession
pithos: wine jar made of earthenware
pletrion: room for gymnastic exercises
polos: crown of cylindrical shape worn by goddesses
*proxenos (*pl. *proxenoi):* p. 269
rhabduchoi: umpires, judges, wearing the staff of office

GLOSSARY OF GREEK WORDS

Seilenos: Silenus
Selene: goddess of the moon
silphion: extinct unbelliferous plant, the juice of which was used in food
    and medicine
skiadiske, skiadeion: parasol, anything that shades
spondauloi: flute players accompanying the sacrifices
spondophoros: herald
stadion: stadion, stade, linear measure ca. 580 ft. (192 m.)

Tetragonon: quadrangle
theokoloi: p. 261
Thyia: p. 25
thymiateria: containers in which incense is burned

Xyleus: p. 258

Zeus Horkios: p. 195